Contents

Introduction ....

    Identifying more able mathematicians 2

    Providing for more able mathematicians 4

    Introducing *Abacus Evolve Challenge* 6

    Using the *Challenge* resources 8

    Icon guide 9

Support for Assessing Pupils' Progress 10

***Talk Maths Extra* pupil software** 14

***Solve the Problem* pupil software** 16

Assessment Activities 18

    Using and applying mathematics 21

    Counting and understanding numbers 22

    Knowing and understanding number facts 23

    Calculating 24

    Understanding shape 25

    Measuring 26

    Handling data 27

Teacher notes 28

Photocopy masters 118

Giftedness and higher ability in Key Stage 1

Many feel that children in this age group are too young to be labelled as 'gifted'. However, there are certainly children who are more able. There are particular difficulties with identifying more able children in Key Stage 1. For example: children's performance in tests and assessed activities may be highly influenced by the classroom environment and by other factors such as home background; there can be a pronounced difference between children's cognitive and physical development; high levels of mathematical understanding may be masked by poor basic numeracy or literacy skills; children's potential ability will manifest at different rates; and it is more likely at Key Stage 1 than at Key Stage 2 that you will find children who display high ability in one area of maths but not another.

What characteristics might more able mathematicians display?

More able mathematicians are likely to have good powers of logic, reasoning and deduction, and will be able to hypothesise, experiment and categorise. This list of questions may be useful in establishing mathematical ability:

- Do they enjoy number puzzles?
- Do they show a good awareness of patterns and sequences?
- Do they ask interesting mathematical questions?
- Do they give explanations you may not have thought of?
- Are they good at solving problems?
- Are they good at applying knowledge in unfamiliar contexts?
- Do they like to choose their own methods?

This list is by no means exhaustive; there are many more characteristics that may be observed in more able mathematicians, and many able children will display only some of these qualities. For example, a child who you believe to be a high achiever may not show advanced problem-solving skills. This may be because they don't yet know how to set about solving a problem, because they haven't learned the strategies required.

What about children who don't show any of these traits?

There may be highly able mathematicians in your class who do not display any of these characteristics. This could be due to one or more of these factors:

- lack of confidence
- unwillingness to stand out from their peers
- the desire to avoid 'extra' work
- an insufficiently stimulating learning environment
- lack of challenging activities
- lack of familiarity with basic number facts and skills
- language barriers
- problems with reading and/or writing.

What can be done to identify more able mathematicians?

Here are a few suggestions of practical steps that can be taken:

- Ask parents and carers to supply information about any mathematical abilities they have noticed at home. In the early years of schooling, it is especially important to involve parents or carers as early on as possible. They are likely to have observed unusual strengths in their children and this information can be key in identifying the more able early on.
- Conduct a brief interview with children at the beginning of the school year to find out about their interests and anything they think they are especially good at.
- Keep a good record of what you observe children doing and saying in practical maths activities.
- Keep a portfolio of particularly good work completed either at home or in school. This will help to assess progress and spot patterns.
- Testing can provide evidence of high ability, but it is important to remember that, especially at Key Stage 1, some very able children may not perform well in tests, and many factors can affect children's performance in a test environment.

The identification–provision cycle

A two-way process of identification and provision is needed. You will not be able to observe exceptional abilities in children unless they are given the opportunity to demonstrate them. Activities must be provided that challenge children and allow them the scope to show what they can do. In this way, appropriate provision leads to identification, which in turn allows you to make better provision.

We recommend that at the beginning of each topic you include the whole class in an activity that gives opportunities for children to take the work as far as they can. This will allow you to identify the children who are more able in that area of maths. (See the assessment activities on pages 18–27.)

Providing for more able mathematicians

How can a stimulating learning environment be created?

It is important to create an atmosphere in which children feel they are able to ask questions, and have access to resources to find the answers. One practical thing you can do is to create interactive displays, or perhaps a 'Challenge corner': an area of the classroom where you can set out maths resources, puzzles, problem-solving scenarios, prompts and questions for children to explore. This should be accessible by all children in the class, giving everyone the opportunity to challenge themselves. If you have a 'role play' corner, this can provide lots of opportunities for children to use and apply mathematics in real-life contexts.

How can questions be used?

More able children should be asked probing and open-ended questions. These will allow you to assess and extend their understanding, get them to think more deeply, and lead them to continue their explorations. Here are some examples of the types of question you might ask:

- What do you think will happen if …?
- How many different ways can you …?
- Is it always true that …?
- Why?
- What patterns can you see?
- Why did you choose to work it out like that?
- Why do you think this happens?
- How do you know that?
- Can you make up a rule?

Children should be encouraged to ask these sorts of question themselves.

What are 'challenge' activities?

'Challenging' work can be defined as something difficult that requires the learner to learn something new. For children to enjoy a challenging activity there must be something about it that motivates them. For example, it could be about a subject that they are particularly interested in, or it could be placed in a meaningful context, with a goal that has nothing to do with completing a page of calculations. The level of challenge must be just right – it must stretch them without being so difficult that children are demotivated and want to give up. The best challenge activities will allow different levels of outcome, so that a wide range of children can succeed at them.

More able children need to be given opportunities to:

- be creative
- exercise their curiosity and explore new ideas
- choose their own ways of working and representing their results
- ask questions and find the answers
- make conjectures and test them out
- discuss their ideas with adults and other children
- reflect on their own work.

More able mathematicians are likely to acquire new skills more quickly than their peers. If they are then asked to practise these skills for too long, they may lose interest. More able mathematicians are also likely to be able to spot quicker or more efficient ways to work things out, and they should be encouraged to explore their chosen methods.

How should children record their work?

Where possible, give children the opportunity to choose how they record their workings and answers: in writing; in pictures; in diagrams; using ICT; taking photographs; or using physical objects such as cubes. As often as possible, leave a variety of equipment on the table when children are taking part in activities, and make it clear that they can choose anything they wish to record their thinking.

What thinking skills should more able children be using?

More able children need to be given opportunities to access their higher-order thinking skills. Bloom's Taxonomy identifies six levels of thinking:

- knowledge – the acquisition and recall of facts
- comprehension – the ability to describe what you know in your own words
- application – the application of what you have learned in context
- analysis – for example, categorising things and identifying patterns
- synthesis – the creation of new ideas or products
- evaluation – the evaluation of ideas, processes and products.

The first three are generally thought of as lower-order skills, although application requires a deeper level of thinking than the first two. If you can plan activities that incorporate the three higher-order thinking skills, children will be challenged.

Introducing *Abacus Evolve Challenge*

What is *Abacus Evolve Challenge*?

Abacus Evolve Challenge is designed to stretch and motivate more able mathematicians. The activities are creative and engaging, and offer opportunities for written, verbal and practical work. Using and applying skills are practised throughout, with plenty of open-ended investigations and problem solving. Speaking and listening skills are promoted through the high proportion of paired and group work.

Which children is *Challenge* for?

Challenge is not just for those children who would be classed as 'gifted'. The activities have been written with the whole of the 'top table' in mind. Differentiation by outcome is often possible because of the open-ended nature of the activities, and the teacher notes accompanying the activities usually suggest ways to differentiate further.

What types of enrichment and extension are provided?

 Breadth – allows children to experience additional material outside of the core offering, rehearse ideas in different contexts, and make connections between areas of maths.

 Depth – is achieved by asking children to delve deeper into the concepts. It is about thinking intellectually.

 Pace – refers to speed in covering the curriculum and can result in achievement at a level exceptional for the age range.

What types of activity are provided?

 Adult-led – these activities allow children to work with an adult. There are two adult-led activities per two-week block.

 Game – these activities allow children to use what they have learned with the rest of the class by playing a game in pairs or groups.

 Problem – these activities allow children to apply their mathematical understanding to solve problems.

 Investigate – these activities allow children to explore a concept freely, asking questions, looking for patterns and drawing conclusions.

When should the *Challenge* activities be used?

There are 90 activities per Year; six for every two-week block. They are intended to be used by small groups of children in the part of the maths lesson when the class is split into groups for differentiated work. This allows the more able children to be included in the whole-class parts of the lesson.

What level of adult support is needed?

The *Challenge* resources have been designed with effective classroom management in mind. Four of the activities in each two-week block can be carried out by children without adult support, allowing you to focus on the other groups. Some of these will require a couple of minutes to get the group started on the activity, but after this children should be able to continue unaided.

Two of the activities in each two-week block require adult support, so that more able children have the benefits of adult input.

How does *Challenge* fit alongside the *Abacus Evolve* maths scheme?

The *Challenge* activities are organised using the same blocked structure as *Abacus Evolve*. You can use the *Abacus Evolve* weekly plans, and fit the *Challenge* activities into these. *Abacus Evolve* objectives are referenced for each activity, and these will help you to decide which core activities to run them alongside. If you also have the *Challenge* Module of I-Planner Online, you will be able to see the *Challenge* activities allocated to suitable days in the weekly plans.

It is intended that the more able children join in with the whole-class parts of the lesson: the mental oral starter, the main teaching activity, and the plenary. When the rest of the class is split up into 1-dot, 2-dot and 3-dot groups to do Textbook activities or practical activities, you can give your top group a *Challenge* activity that fits in well with what the rest of the class are doing.

Can I use *Challenge* with another maths scheme or my own planning?

Although the *Challenge* activities complement *Abacus Evolve* activities, they are not specifically linked to them, so there is no dependence on any part of the *Abacus Evolve* scheme. The *Challenge* activities can be used to accompany any other maths scheme or your own planning. You can search for *Challenge* activities that fit your teaching by looking at the Renewed Framework objectives in the Teacher Guide. All of the Renewed Framework objectives are covered by the *Challenge* activities.

What resources are in the *Challenge* range?

Each Year includes:

- a Teacher Guide
- a Workbook or Textbook
- an I-Planner Online Module.

Teacher Guide

The Teacher Guide contains detailed notes to accompany each activity. The information provided includes:

- Suggested group size and adult support
- Resources required (Workbook pages, Photocopy Masters and other resources)
- *Abacus Evolve* objectives
- Renewed Framework objectives
- A description of the activity
- 'Extra help': ideas for differentiating at a lower level
- 'Further extension': ideas for differentiating at a higher level
- 'If you have time': ideas for continuing the activity
- Background maths information for the non-specialist teacher
- 'Be aware': things to watch out for, such as common misconceptions
- Outcomes for the activity, given in child-friendly language
- Ideas for other resources to support the activity, such as useful websites or stories.

Workbook

Roughly half of the Year 1 *Challenge* activities are accompanied by a Workbook page. The pages are colourful and engaging, and they include the following features:

- speech bubbles to indicate opportunities for discussion
- an Extra activity at the bottom of each page for children who finish early.

The Workbook pages are not just intended for children to use individually. They are usually suitable for paired or group work.

I-Planner Online

The *Abacus Evolve* I-Planner is a powerful online tool that provides ready-to-use weekly, medium-term and yearly plans that are completely flexible. It can save hours of planning time, but allows you to adapt the plans to meet the exact needs of your class. The *Challenge* module of I-Planner for each Year includes an extra column in the weekly plans in which you can see all the *Challenge* activities allocated to suitable days. This allows you to plan the *Challenge* activities seamlessly into your maths lessons.

What support is provided for assessing the children?

The adult-led activities are ideal for day-to-day observational assessment, as they provide plenty of opportunities to work closely with the children and ask probing questions to ascertain their level of understanding.

The charts on pages 10–13 of this book show the Assessment Foci from the Assessing Pupils' Progress guidelines, and the *Challenge* activities that can be used to provide evidence towards this type of periodic assessment.

On pages 18–27 of this book you will find six assessment activities. These will help you to assess prior learning and identify children's potential in each strand of maths.

Icon guide

Group size

 Children working individually, without an adult

 Children working in pairs, without an adult

 Children working in groups, without an adult

 Children working in groups, with an adult

Type of resource

 Workbook

 Photocopy Master

 Additional resources

Type of enrichment/extension

 Breadth

 Depth

 Pace

Type of activity

 Adult-led

Game

Problem

Investigate

Support for Assessing Pupils' Progress

If you are using Assessing Pupils' Progress to assess children, you may find this chart helpful when deciding which of the *Challenge* activities could be used to provide evidence towards each Assessment Focus.

We do not recommend that you use every activity to make an assessment. It is also important to recognise that a full assessment cannot be made on the basis of the *Challenge* activities alone; you will need to draw on other sources of information as well. We would advise that in each block of work you use this chart as guidance towards choosing one activity to assess against APP criteria, to complement other day-to-day or periodic assessments.

Most of the Year 1 *Challenge* activities should give children the opportunity to work at a secure Level 2.

Ma1 Using and applying mathematics

	Problem solving	Communicating	Reasoning
Level 2	• C1.2 Measuring in hands • C1.3 How many feet? • E1.1 Granny's knitting • E1.2 Double-buttoned coat • E1.4 Paying for parking • B2.1 It's in the balance • C2.2 How much is a kilogram? • C2.3 How much is a gram? • A3.1 Fingers and toes • B3.5 Spotting ladybirds • C3.2 How much water in a puddle? • D3.1 On the buses 1 • D3.2 On the buses 2 • D3.3 Football stadium 1 • D3.4 On the buses 3 • E3.4 Going for a ride	• B1.1 … And another one • D1.5 Money banks • E1.5 What did she buy? • E1.6 Money changer • B2.5 Turning around • B2.6 Obstacle course • C2.1 How heavy is a ball? • D2.1 Spot the 3D shapes • D2.4 Fill the box • D2.6 Apple packing • E2.5 Four in a line • A3.2 Fives • C3.1 Spinner fun • C3.3 Rice mice game • C3.6 Time dominoes • D3.1 On the buses 1 • D3.3 Football stadium 1 • E3.5 Zina's change	• A1.6 Biggest, smallest • B1.1 … And another one • D1.3 Shape families • D1.4 Caterpillars • A2.5 Beads • A2.6 Between • B2.2 Hidden numbers • B2.3 Shortcuts • D2.2 Making dice • D2.3 The shape sorter • D2.4 Fill the box • D2.5 Four dice • A3.5 Who won the race? • B3.1 Chasing 9 • B3.4 Missing digits • B3.5 Spotting ladybirds • B3.6 Investigating ladybirds • E3.1 Counting in 2s and 5s • E3.3 Odds and evens • E3.6 Special offers
Level 1	• C1.1 Spiral worms	• A1.3 Finders keepers • C1.5 Week wheel • C1.6 Month wheel • D1.1 Where are the shapes? • D1.2 What's my picture?	• B1.6 Totals of 7 • C1.4 Days of the week

Ma2 Number

	Numbers and the number system	Fractions	Operations, relationships between them
Level 2	• A1.1 Washing lines • A1.4 Coin collector • A1.5 Parcel post • A1.6 Biggest, smallest • D1.4 Caterpillars • A2.1 Number words • A2.2 Counting in 10s • A2.3 10 more, 10 less • E2.1 Caterpillars • E2.2 Counter act • E2.3 Choosing tracks • A3.2 Fives • A3.4 Work out my number • A3.5 Who won the race? • A3.6 In between • E3.1 Counting in 2s and 5s • E3.2 Threes • E3.3 Odds and evens		• B2.1 It's in the balance
Level 1		• C3.1 Spinner fun • C3.3 Rice mice game	• B1.3 Cube scores • B1.4 Round and round • D1.6 Skittles

Ma2 Number

		Mental methods	Solving numerical problems	Written methods
Level 2		• E1.3 Next door numbers • B2.2 Hidden numbers • B2.3 Shortcuts • D2.5 Four dice • D2.6 Apple packing • E2.5 Four in a line • A3.3 Adding 10s game • B3.1 Chasing 9 • B3.3 Countdown • B3.4 Missing digits • B3.6 Investigating ladybirds • D3.2 On the buses 2 • D3.5 I spy … • D3.6 Football stadium 2	• A1.2 Purses • A1.4 Coin collector • D1.5 Money banks • E1.1 Granny's knitting • E1.2 Double-buttoned coat • E1.4 Paying for parking • E1.5 What did she buy? • E1.6 Money changer • E2.4 Take-away menu • E2.6 Number lines • B3.2 Numbers, words and pictures • D3.4 On the buses 3 • D3.5 I spy … • D3.6 Football stadium 2 • E3.4 Going for a ride • E3.5 Zina's change • E3.6 Special offers	• E2.6 Number lines • B3.3 Countdown
Level 1		• B1.2 Hop, skip and jump • B1.5 Six in a line • B1.6 Totals of 7	• B1.4 Round and round • B1.5 Six in a line • D1.6 Skittles	• B1.2 Hop, skip and jump • B1.3 Cube scores

Ma3 Shape, space and measures

	Properties of shape	Properties of position and movement	Measures
Level 2	• D1.3 Shape families • D2.1 Spot the 3D shapes • D2.2 Making dice • D2.3 The shape sorter	• A2.4 Colouring to order • A2.5 Beads • A2.6 Between • B2.5 Turning around • B2.6 Obstacle course	• C1.2 Measuring in hands • C1.3 How many feet? • C2.1 How heavy is a ball? • C2.2 How much is a kilogram? • C2.3 How much is a gram? • C2.4 Analogue and digital pelmanism • C3.2 How much water in a puddle? • C3.3 Rice mice game • C3.4 Half past • C3.5 How many minutes? • C3.6 Time dominoes
Level 1	• D1.1 Where are the shapes? • D1.2 What's my picture?	• B2.4 What's my number?	• C1.1 Spiral worms • C1.4 Days of the week • C1.5 Week wheel • C1.6 Month wheel

Ma4 Handling data

	Processing and representing data	Interpreting data
Level 2	• C2.5 Coin pictogram • C2.6 Favourite colours	• C2.5 Coin pictogram • C2.6 Favourite colours

Abacus Evolve *Talk Maths Extra* will reinforce key maths skills and get children talking about maths.

1 Counting in 10s 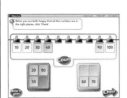	Complete a sequence counting on in 10s from 10 to 100.	**2 Making amounts** 
Make amounts in a given range with 1p and 10p coins.	**3 Addition facts** 	Partition a small number in different ways by placing blue and green counters in a tray.

4 Sorting shapes 	Sort 2D shapes into two sets according to their properties.	**5 Counting in 10s** 
Complete a sequence counting on or back in 10s from a 1-digit number.	**6 Ordering numbers** 	Place numbers less than 40 onto a rack, aiming to end up with the numbers in order.

7 Addition facts 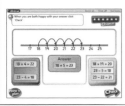	Place dominoes so that touching ends add up to the same total.	**8 Printing shapes** 
Work out which prints could be made using faces, edges and corners of 3D shapes.	**9 Counting on and back** 	Complete number sequences counting on and back in 1s up to 50.

10 Addition and subtraction 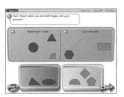	Find the sentence that matches an addition or subtraction shown on a number line.	**11 Place value** 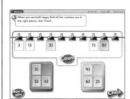
Make target numbers by adding tens and units.	**12 Addition and subtraction facts** 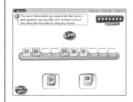	Make target numbers up to 20 by adding and subtracting small numbers.

13 Number puzzle 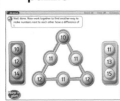	Place numbers so that each pair of adjacent numbers has a difference of 1.	**14 Word problems** 
Fill in numbers in a word problem to make a correct addition or subtraction.	**15 Counting in 2s and 5s** 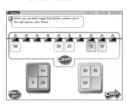	Complete a sequence counting on or back in 2s or 5s.

16 Estimating quantities 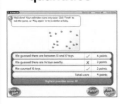	Estimate a number of objects, then count them.	**17 Toy shelves** 
Follow clues to position toys on a shelf.	**18 Block graph** 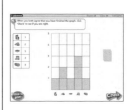	Build a block graph to match given data.

This chart shows which *Talk Maths Extra* activities could be used to extend some of the Challenge activities. The 4-dot version of each *Talk Maths Extra* activity is likely to be the most suitable for your children.

Challenge activity	Related *Talk Maths Extra* activities
A1.1 Washing lines	11 Place value
A1.2 Purses	1 Counting in 10s
A1.4 Coin collector	2 Making amounts, 11 Place value
A1.6 Biggest, smallest	6 Ordering numbers
B1.3 Cube scores	3 Addition facts
B1.6 Totals of 7	3 Addition facts, 7 Addition facts
D1.2 What's my picture?	4 Sorting shapes
D1.3 Shape families	4 Sorting shapes
D1.4 Caterpillars	6 Ordering numbers
D1.5 Which money bank?	2 Making amounts
D1.6 Skittles	12 Addition and subtraction facts
E1.4 Paying for parking	2 Making amounts
A2.1 Number words	11 Place value
A2.2 Counting in 10s	1 Counting in 10s, 5 Counting in 10s
A2.3 10 more, 10 less	5 Counting in 10s, 9 Counting on and back
A2.6 Between	6 Ordering numbers
B2.1 It's in the balance	3 Addition facts, 7 Addition facts
B2.3 Shortcuts	3 Addition facts, 7 Addition facts
B2.4 What's my number?	17 Toy shelves
B2.6 Obstacle course	17 Toy shelves
C2.6 Favourite colours	18 Block graph
D2.2 Making dice	8 Printing shapes
D2.3 The shape sorter	8 Printing shapes
D2.4 Fill the box	9 Counting on and back
D2.5 Four dice	9 Counting on and back, 12 Addition and subtraction facts
E2.1 Caterpillars	1 Counting in 10s, 5 Counting in 10s
E2.4 Take-away menu	10 Addition and subtraction, 14 Word problems
E2.5 Four in a line	9 Counting on and back, 10 Addition and subtraction
E2.6 Number lines	10 Addition and subtraction, 14 Word problems
A3.1 Fingers and toes	15 Counting in 2s and 5s
A3.3 Adding 10s game	15 Counting in 2s and 5s
A3.4 What's my number?	11 Place value
A3.5 Who won the race?	11 Place value
A3.6 In between	6 Ordering numbers
B3.1 Chasing 9	12 Addition and subtraction facts
B3.3 Countdown	12 Addition and subtraction facts
B3.5 Spotting ladybirds	12 Addition and subtraction facts, 13 Number puzzle
B3.6 Investigating ladybirds	12 Addition and subtraction facts, 13 Number puzzle
D3.1 On the buses 1	12 Addition and subtraction facts, 16 Estimating quantities
D3.2 On the buses 2	10 Addition and subtraction, 12 Addition and subtraction facts
D3.5 I spy ...	11 Place value, 14 Word problems
E3.1 Counting in 2s and 5s	15 Counting in 2s and 5s

Solve the Problem pupil software

Abacus Evolve *Solve the Problem* will challenge children with rich, open-ended problems that draw on a range of mathematical strategies.

Build a Railway

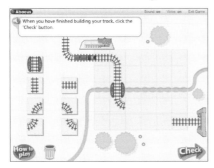

Children are asked to build a railway track from the station to the tunnel using different shaped pieces. They can be set different challenges, such as using a certain number or certain type of pieces. They then test their tracks to see if they work.

Bus Journey

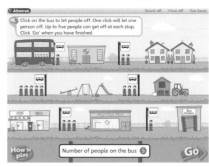

A bus is travelling along its route. At each stop, a certain number of people get on, and the children decide how many people will get off at each stop. The aim is for the bus to arrive at the end of its journey with the target number of people on board.

The Quangle Wangle's Tea Party

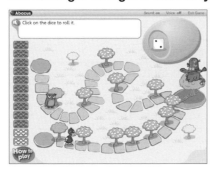

Quangle Wangle invites Owl and Duck to a tea party. He asks them to bring jam sandwiches, which grow (in groups of 10) on trees along the way. Children must partition the number rolled on the dice so that Owl and Duck together visit the trees they wanted.

Patchwork Blanket

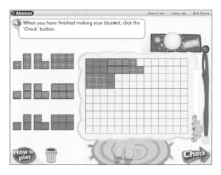

Children make a patchwork blanket by dragging patches of different size, shape and colour onto a grid. The challenge is not to place any patches of the same colour next to each other. Children can then try again, using fewer shapes and/or colours.

Treasure Hunt

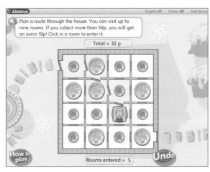

Children are given the plan of a house with sixteen rooms. Each room contains either 1p or 10p. They work out a route through the house, visiting up to nine adjacent rooms. If they collect more than 50p, they win a 10p bonus..

Birthday Party

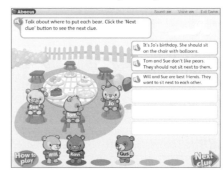

The context is a bears' birthday party. A table has been set with places for six bears. Children are given clues to help them decide where each bear should sit. Children can play the game twice; the second time they will receive a different set of clues.

This chart shows which *Solve the Problem* activities could be used to extend some of the Challenge activities. The *Solve the Problem* activities are suitable for all ability levels, as children can set their own problems.

Challenge activity	Related *Solve the Problem* activities
A1.2 Purses	The Quangle Wangle's Tea Party, Treasure Hunt
A1.3 Finders keepers	The Quangle Wangle's Tea Party, Treasure Hunt
B1.1 ... And another one	Bus Journey
B1.2 Hop, skip and jump	Bus Journey
B1.3 Cube scores	Bus Journey
B1.4 Round and round	The Quangle Wangle's Tea Party
D1.2 What's my picture?	Patchwork Blanket
D1.3 Shape families	Patchwork Blanket
D1.4 Caterpillars	Treasure Hunt
D1.5 Which money bank?	Bus Journey, Treasure Hunt
D1.6 Skittles	Bus Journey
E1.5 What did she buy?	Treasure Hunt
A2.2 Counting in 10s	The Quangle Wangle's Tea Party, Treasure Hunt
A2.3 10 more, 10 less	Treasure Hunt
B2.1 It's in the balance	The Quangle Wangle's Tea Party
B2.2 Hidden numbers	The Quangle Wangle's Tea Party
B2.4 What's my number?	Build a Railway, Patchwork Blanket, Birthday Party
B2.5 Turning around	Build a Railway
B2.6 Obstacle course	Build a Railway, Patchwork Blanket, Birthday Party
D2.4 Fill the box	Bus Journey
D2.6 Apple packing	The Quangle Wangle's Tea Party, Treasure Hunt
E2.1 Caterpillars	The Quangle Wangle's Tea Party, Treasure Hunt
E2.2 Counter act	The Quangle Wangle's Tea Party, Treasure Hunt
E2.3 Choosing tracks	The Quangle Wangle's Tea Party, Treasure Hunt
E2.4 Take-away menu	Bus Journey
E2.5 Four in a line	Bus Journey
E2.6 Number lines	Bus Journey
A3.3 Adding 10s game	The Quangle Wangle's Tea Party
B3.1 Chasing 9	Bus Journey
B3.3 Countdown	Bus Journey
D3.1 On the buses 1	Build a Railway, Bus Journey, Birthday Party
D3.2 On the buses 2	Bus Journey
D3.4 On the buses 3	Bus Journey, Treasure Hunt

Assessment Activities

What do the six assessment activities cover?

In Key Stage 1, some children may perform very well in some areas of maths, and not so well in others. This is why we have provided six assessment activities, one for each strand of maths. These activities are intended to help you to assess children's prior learning and identify children with the potential to perform at a high level in maths. The activities allow for a mixture of ways to suit the needs of the children and to enable them to express their mathematical understanding appropriately. The outcomes of these activities may help you to decide which children should be in your 'Challenge' group for each strand.

Why is there no assessment activity for Using & applying?

There is no separate assessment activity for the Using and applying mathematics strand. Instead, Using & Applying is embedded in the six activities, and some guidance is given below about what to look out for when trying to identify exceptional Using & Applying skills. Sometimes, gifted or more able mathematicians may have poor basic numeracy skills, so their ability may not be evident. Focusing on these children's Using & Applying skills can be a good way to identify their potential.

Which children should take part in the assessment activities?

The assessment activities are designed to be accessible for every child in the class. They are intended to give all children the chance to demonstrate their mathematical understanding, and thereby help you to identify those children who have the potential to perform at a high level.

When should the assessment activities be used?

The timing of the assessment activities is up to you. Here are some examples of when and how you might choose to use them.

- Carry out each activity at the beginning of a related block of work. The table below shows when each strand is covered throughout the year.
- Carry out one or two activities per term, spreading the six activities across the whole year.
- Carry out all six activities several times throughout the year, for example at the beginning of each term. This may help you to monitor children's progress from term to term.

This table shows the Abacus Evolve blocks in which each strand is covered in Year 1.

Strand	Abacus Evolve blocks		
	Autumn	Spring	Summer
Using and applying mathematics	Embedded throughout		
Counting and understanding number	A1, B1, D1	A2, E2	A3
Knowing and using number facts	A1, B1, D1, E1	A2, B2, E2	B3, E3
Calculating	B1, D1	A2, B2, D2, E2	A3, B3, D3, E3
Understanding shape	D1	B2, D2	
Measuring	C1	C2	C3
Handling data		C2	

How are the assessment activities structured?

There are two parts to each activity: a core activity and an extension activity. It is intended that the core activity is carried out by all the children. This part of the activity should allow you to identify those children who are ready for something a bit more challenging. Those children can be moved on to the extension activity, while the rest of the class continue with the core activity. The extension activity should help you to see which children have exceptional mathematical understanding, and therefore may benefit from the Challenge activities in this book.

What guidance is given for the assessment activities?

Within the core activity, suggestions are given for questions that could be asked or things that might be observed that may indicate which children have a higher level of understanding. These assessment points should aid you in deciding which children to move on to the extension activity.

For the extension activity, suggestions are provided for things that you might observe and things that children might say that could indicate that they have the potential to perform at a high level in that area of maths. Some of these assessment points are specific to that strand, and some are related to Using & Applying.

Some guidance is given as to the National Curriculum levels children may be working at, based on Assessment Foci from Assessing Pupils' Progress (APP). However, as noted below, the principle purpose of these activities is not to assign levels to children.

How should the activities be observed?

The activities are intended to be carried out in small groups, with an adult moving from group to group. Giving children an opportunity to try out activities in small groups can offer opportunities to observe their ability to collaborate, the extent to which they understand key words and their ability to communicate with others. It can also reveal their ability to concentrate and understand the task. Recording what children say and do is an essential part of any assessment, particularly of younger children. Recording children working together using sound or video can greatly ease the burden of recording.

How can the assessment activities be used to promote Speaking & Listening?

The idea of these activities is that within a structured play environment the focus can be firmly set within Speaking & Listening. The assessment therefore is based on the spoken interactions which demonstrate problem-solving skills through dialogue with peers. This ensures that every child has the opportunity to participate in the activities.

Should the assessment activities involve mark making?

During the activities it may be helpful to allow children to record their ideas, perhaps in a blank book so that they are not restricted by squares or lines. Giving children opportunities to select and record their work in the most appropriate way is an important part of any maths activity. Being able to link their words and their number sentences to diagrams and pictures is a crucial step in their development. Using this to assess over a period of time through a careful analysis of their work can be revealing and help to identify those children who like to record in different ways.

Are there any Challenge assessment tests?

Young children's high ability in maths is not always evident via testing. Their ability can be masked by factors such as poor numeracy or literacy skills, and children's performance can be greatly affected by particular circumstances on the day of testing. Therefore these children will not always perform well in a test environment, or against National Curriculum level descriptors in less formal assessments. Children with latent abilities in maths may exhibit a range of skills that relate to Using & Applying, such as thinking skills, creativity, and the ability to explain their ideas, which are best assessed through observation.

Can I use the assessment activities to assign National Curriculum levels?

The main purpose of these assessment activities is to give all children – those who may not perform well against the National Curriculum level descriptors as well as those that do – an opportunity to display their skills in collaborative problem solving, Speaking & Listening and personal learning and thinking skills as areas that might identify them as more able. It may be inappropriate to assign National Curriculum levels to these activities, although they could be used to support APP if required.

How can I assess the progress of children in the 'Challenge' group?

The Challenge activities on pages 28–117 of this book can be used to provide evidence of children's ongoing progress. The adult-led activities will be particularly useful for this purpose. If your school is using APP for periodic assessment, you may find the charts on pages 10–13 of this book helpful. These charts show you which of the Challenge activities could be used to provide evidence towards each of the Assessment Foci, with an indication of the levels that could be achieved by children taking part in the activities.

While there are no assessment tests included in the Challenge resources, there are plenty of assessment materials readily available that can be used alongside the Challenge activities. For example, within the core *Abacus Evolve* scheme you will find:

- Review Tasks: these can be used to assess children's prior learning at the start of a week, topic or block.
- Assessment Tasks: these can be used with groups to determine children's understanding from observation and questioning, and they are linked to APP.
- Assessment Tests: these are mental and written tests that allow you to track progress more formally.

Using and applying mathematics

Using and applying mathematics is the strand that is likely to offer the most useful opportunities for identifying gifted and able children.

All of the assessment activities incorporate aspects of Using & Applying and therefore all of the activities have guidance at the end of the activity with suggestions for the types of learning that might be needed to successfully use and apply mathematics within the task.

The extension activity which is embedded in each task offers particular opportunities for children to extend their learning and enrich their experiences into areas which are perhaps less familiar to them.

Look out for children who:

- grasp what the problem is
- know how to get started
- develop systems
- can describe their strategies clearly
- record in ways that help them to explain their ideas
- use a range of mathematical vocabulary within the context
- predict an outcome and then test it
- are interested in other ways of working
- see patterns in numbers and shapes
- see relationships between the work at the beginning of the activity and the work at the end
- use their earlier experiences to tackle more challenging activities
- are good leaders within the group (although some able children prefer to work alone)
- listen and respond to the ideas of others in the group
- are not afraid to try things out and then modify or change their ideas.

Children demonstrate many of the aspects of Using & Applying at Level 2 if they can:

- select the mathematics they use in the activity
- discuss their work using mathematical language
- represent their work using symbols and simple diagrams
- predict what comes next
- explain why an answer is correct
- give reasons for their opinions.

Children demonstrate many of the aspects of Using & Applying at Level 1 if they can:

- use mathematics as an integral part of the activity
- represent their work with objects or pictures
- discuss their work
- draw simple conclusions from their work
- recognise and use simple patterns or relationships.

Counting and understanding numbers

Resources
Modelling clay; plastic knives; rolling pins

Core activity
Arrange children into pairs. Give one child in each pair some modelling clay, and ask them to make a pizza from it. *In this activity, you are going to be sharing the pizza equally between you and your partner.* Ask pairs to divide their pizzas as equally as possible between the two of them. Then ask them to record what they have done, in any way they choose. Encourage children to discuss in their pairs how they shared their pizzas. Note any children who are using the word *half* and how they are recording this. Ask these children to explain a half to the others.

Extension activity
This time, you are going to share your pizzas with two more children; so it will be shared between four people in total. How will you do this? How much pizza will each person have? Observe children to see if they start again or if they halve the halves. Note any children who use the word *quarter* and how they record this. Now ask children to share the pizza with four more children. *There are now eight children and one pizza – how will you share it? How many other ways could you share the pizza? Are some numbers of people harder to share between? Why?*

Look out for children who:
- use different ways of creating a pizza, e.g. circular, rectangular, square
- understand that sharing between two means splitting into two equal parts
- build on the work they have already completed to solve further problems, e.g splitting each half into two to make four quarters
- use notation and understand the meaning within the context of pizzas, e.g. *half a pizza*
- can relate this activity to other experiences they have had, e.g. sharing a piece of cake with a sibling
- listen to the ideas of the group before making decisions
- draw diagrams to explain what they have done
- ask each other questions
- think of different options and consider several of them before commencing the problem.

Look out for ideas such as:
- *If we cut this pizza in two down the middle we will both have half.*
- *If we cut the halves in half we will have enough for four people – that's fair.*
- *I think a quarter of a pizza is enough for you. I'll keep these two quarters. That leaves a quarter for someone else! Is that fair?*

This activity could provide evidence towards the following Assessment Foci from APP:

Ma2 Number	
Fractions	
Level 2	• Are children beginning to use the concept of a fraction, for example by sharing their pizza into halves and quarters? • Can children relate the concept of half of a small quantity to the concept of half of a shape, for example by drawing a diagram of a circle and shading half of it?
Level 1	• Are children beginning to use the fraction one-half, for example when talking about sharing their pizza between two children?

Knowing and understanding number facts

Resources
A collection of counters in various colours and sizes; a jar; envelopes

Core activity
Show children a jar containing 20 counters. Ask each child to guess the number of counters. When they have each had a turn at guessing, tip the counters out onto the table and ask children to decide how many counters there actually are. *How do you know?*

Extension activity
Give each pair an envelope and 20 counters. Ask them to take turns to hide some of the counters in the envelope. They challenge their partner to work out how many are missing. Ask them to record this as a number sentence and explain it to their partner.

Repeat the activity with a different number of counters, increasing the number as appropriate up to 100. Ask children to make up a number sentence to explain what is happening.

Set them a *What if* question such as: *What if there were 20 dinosaurs, rather than counters? What if there were red, blue and yellow counters, how would you count the total number now? What if there were big and small counters? Does it matter? Why?*

Look out for children who:
- use groups to help them count, e.g. 2s, 5s or 10s
- find quick ways of checking their accuracy, e.g. organising the groups into piles
- use patterns to help them count, e.g. five counters organised like spots on a dice
- use original examples to explain their counting patterns to others
- recognise doubles or numbers of groups to help to count, e.g. two groups of five
- systematically group the remaining counters to know how many counters are hidden
- realise that the size and shape of the counters is not relevant to the overall 'count'
- begin to change the context of their number sentences from counters to other things
- are happy to try working with larger numbers
- ask their partner how they have checked their answer
- ask questions
- have one idea and then change it for a different one.

Look out for ideas such as:
- *I think there are 20 counters because there are four groups of five.*
- *I think there are 20 because there are two groups of 10.*
- *I disagree – I think there are 20 because there are 10 groups of two.*

This activity could provide evidence towards the following Assessment Foci from APP:

	Ma2 Number			
	Numbers and the number system	**Operations, relationships between them**	**Mental methods**	**Written methods**
Level 2	• Can they count the objects reliably, perhaps using grouping to help them?	• Do they understand that subtraction is the inverse of addition?	• Can they use addition and subtraction facts to 10 to help them to make number sentences?	• Do they record their work in writing, for example using number sentences?
Level 1	• Can they estimate and count up to 10 objects?	• Do they understand addition as finding a total, and subtraction as taking away?	• Can they add and subtract numbers of objects up to 10?	• Do they record their work using objects, pictures, diagrams or symbols?

Calculating

Resources
A collection of pennies; items with price labels

Core activity
Organise children into pairs. Give each child 20 pennies. Ask them to organise the pennies in such a way that their partner will know how much they have got without the need to count. Observe how they organise the pennies and ask them to record how they know there is 20p. In pairs, children take turns to be 'shopkeeper' and 'shopper': one child buys an item and pays the shopkeeper the money, and then they swap. *Who has got the most / least money after you have done your shopping?* Ask children to write a number sentence to explain what they did and to 'tell the story' of the number sentence to their partner. For example: *I had 20p in my purse, then I bought a pencil for 10p so now I have 10p left.*

Extension activity
Challenge each pair to spend all their money so that they have none left. They can buy any items they like and they can buy more than one of each item. Ask them to make a 'bill' to show how they spent their money. They then compare their 'bill' with their partner's.
How many different ways are there to spend 20p? What if you had 5p more? How many more choices would this give you? How do you know?

Look out for children who:
- sort their money systematically to help them to count and check
- use groups to help them count, e.g. 2s, 5s and 10s
- work systematically to choose items that are for sale at the best price
- understand that when they spend their money and give it to the shopkeeper the shopkeeper gains that amount of money
- realise that they would have more choice if they had more money
- begin to ask if they can add different items to the shopping list to make more choice
- relate the problem to a range of real experiences, such as shopping outside school
- ask each other questions
- think of different options and consider several of them before commencing the problem.

Look out for ideas such as:
- *I started with 20p and then I spent 12p. I have 8p left.*
- *I started with 20p and then I spent 10p so I know that I have spent half of my money.*
- *I started with 20p and I bought two things that cost 5p each. So I know I have 10p left.*

This activity could provide evidence towards the following Assessment Foci from APP:

Ma2 Number			
Operations, relationships between them	**Mental methods**	**Solving numerical problems**	**Written methods**
Level 2 • Do they understand that subtraction is the inverse of addition?	• Can they use addition and subtraction facts to 10 and doubling/halving to help them?	• Can they work out whether to add or subtract to solve a problem? • Can they solve money problems?	• Do they record their work in writing, for example using number sentences?
Level 1 • Do they understand addition as finding a total, and subtraction as taking away?	• Are they beginning to know some addition facts?	• Can they solve addition and subtraction problems involving small numbers?	• Do they record their work using objects, pictures, diagrams or symbols?

Understanding shape

Resources
2D shapes; 3D shapes; real-life 3D objects such as glue-sticks, chocolate boxes, cereal boxes, dice; vocabulary cards (these can photocopied from PCMs 11 and 17); hoops

Core activity
Give each group one set of shapes/objects from the list above, some vocabulary cards and some sorting hoops. Ask them to group the objects in any way they like. Which children come up with ideas for grouping the objects? Can they explain their reasons? Which children know the names and features of common 2D or 3D shapes?

Tell children that you are going to put the shapes away in a few minutes and you want them to record their groups on paper. Ask them to use this to explain their groups to a partner.

Extension activity
Ask children to sort objects using a grid like this.
Do children know which shapes are 3D and which are not?
Can they define 3D?

	3D shapes	Not 3D shapes

If children are successful at this then ask them to sort the objects again using a grid like this.
Are children able to sort the shapes using two criteria? Which children know how to split one group into two rather than starting from scratch?

	3D shapes	Not 3D shapes
Red		
Not red		

Look out for children who:
- use a variety of different ways of classifying the same objects
- use props such as the vocabulary cards without being asked to do so
- begin to add new objects to the game and test out their groupings
- use original ways of recording that make sense to them, and explain them to others
- amend and build on their previous ideas
- ask their partner about their ideas
- recognise a good idea in what others say or do
- openly discuss their difficulties
- have one idea and then change it for another one
- begin to adapt and change the activity for something more complex.

Look out for ideas such as:
- *I think all 3D objects are fat, not flat.*
- *I disagree – what about this sponge?*
- *But is it 3D? What does that mean?*

This activity could provide evidence towards the following Assessment Foci from APP:

	Ma3 Shape, Space and Measures	Ma4 Handling data
	Properties of shape	Processing and representing data
Level 2	• Do children use mathematical names for 2D and 3D shapes? • Can children describe the properties of 2D and 3D shapes, for example talking about their sides, corners, edges, faces?	• Can children sort 2D and 3D shapes into groups according to more than one criterion?
Level 1	• Do children use everyday language to describe 2D and 3D shapes, for example *large, small, flat, round*?	• Can they sort and classify 2D and 3D shapes and explain their criteria?

Measuring

Resources
Colouring pencils of different lengths; items to use for measuring, e.g. linking cubes, long strips of paper, rulers

Core activity
Organise children into pairs. Give each pair a set of colouring pencils and ask them to sort them into groups. Observe how they set about this task and listen to their reasons for sorting them in their chosen ways. Focus on a pair who have sorted the pencils by length and ask that pair to explain what they have done. Explain to everyone that you want them all to focus on length and to order their objects from shortest to longest.
Put some items for measuring on the table, and explain that children can use them if they wish.

Extension activity
When each pair have organised their pencils by length, ask them to work with another pair. *Can you combine your two groups together to make one group?* Point to a pair of pencils side by side. *Which of these is longer? Can you explain how much longer this pencil is than that one?*
When they have completed the task, ask them to record what they have done so that when they put the pencils away they can explain to another group how many pencils they had and how they organised them by length.
Now ask children to think about their height. *How could you organise yourselves from tallest to shortest? Can you find out how much taller or shorter you are than someone else?*

Look out for children who:
- can compare two pencils to order them by length
- work systematically to organise the pencils one at a time into an organised set
- can use the phrases *shorter than* and *longer than* within the context
- discuss the difference between *long* and *tall*
- recognise the difficulties of working with pencils that are the same length
- can combine two similar sets by working from one set and including the others
- use non-standard measures to quantify the difference in the length of the pencils, e.g. *longer than six linking cubes*
- begin to ask if they can add different pencils to the set
- relate this activity to other lengths, e.g. the length of their arms
- ask each other questions
- think different options and consider several of them before commencing the problem.

Look out for ideas such as:
- *We don't need to start again because we can use our set and add your set to it.*
- *We can draw round our group of pencils to show what we have done.*
- *We could use strips of paper to compare our heights.*

This activity could provide evidence towards the following Assessment Foci from APP:

Ma3 Shape, Space and Measures	
Measures	
Level 2	• Are children beginning to use everyday standard and non-standard units to measure length, for example comparing the lengths of pencils using linking cubes?
Level 1	• Can children measure and order objects using direct comparison, for example holding two pencils side by side and saying which is longer?

Handling data

Resources
Squared paper; plain paper; pencils

Core activity
The school council has decided to set up a healthy tuck shop. They need to know which food items to stock in their shop. How could you help them to organise this so that they are successful? Work in groups of four to come up with some ideas to help them.

Collate the ideas from each group and discuss with the class which idea is most useful. Discuss how advertisers and large companies do surveys to collect information about the best products to sell. Ask children to consider whether a survey would be helpful and then ask each group to decide on the best question to ask. Each group then collects the data from the whole class to answer that question. Observe how children work together to decide on the most useful information and then on how to collect the data.

Extension activity
Once children have collected their data, ask them to organise it in a way that is helpful for the school council. *What is the information telling you? Is it useful? Could it help you to plan the new tuck shop?*
What recommendations would you make to the school council based on the information that you have gathered from the class?

Look out for children who:
- make decisions in their group based on relevance to the problem
- can decide what is useful information
- can pose questions effectively
- make the link between the data from their group and the implications for the class
- recognise that collecting data needs to be organised efficiently
- realise that presenting the data in a clear and concise way is important if other people are going to use it
- recognise that the size of the sample group is important and ask to collect information from other classes
- discuss their ideas in a group and listen to other ideas
- build on the ideas of others to complete the task
- ask each other questions
- think of different options and consider several of them before commencing the problem.

Look out for ideas such as:
- *I think most children in the class will buy apples from the tuck shop.*
- *Let's ask the class how many apples they would buy from the tuck shop in a week.*
- *Let's draw a graph to show the most popular fruits in the class.*

This activity could provide evidence towards the following Assessment Foci from APP:

Ma4 Handling data	
Processing and representing data	**Interpreting data**
Level 2 • Do children understand vocabulary related to handling data? • Can children collect and sort data to test their hypothesis? • Can children record their results using simple lists, tables or graphs?	• Can children communicate their findings, using their lists, tables or graphs?
Level 1 • Can children represent their work, for example using objects or pictures to create a simple bar graph?	• Can children answer questions about the data they have collected?

Challenge Plan: Year 1

A1: counting in 1s up to 100; counting on and back in 10s; recognising the value of digits in a 'teens' number; comparing two numbers

Summary

Y1 ⭐ A1.1

Washing lines

Individuals, pairs or groups working independently

Year 1 Challenge Workbook pages 2 and 3

Blank number cards (optional); 1–30 number line (optional); linking cubes (optional)

Abacus Evolve objectives

- Read numbers up to 20 in words and figures
- Recognise the value of each digit in a 'teens' number
- Write numbers up to 10 in words and up to 11 in figures
- Begin to read numbers up to 100 in words and figures
- Begin to partition 2-digit numbers into T and U

Framework objectives

- *Derive and recall all pairs of numbers with a total of 10 and addition facts for totals to at least 5; work out the corresponding subtraction facts*

Teacher notes

Preparation
Cut a sheet of A4 paper into four or more equal pieces for children to use as blank number cards if they reach the Extra activity.

Getting started
Show children the washing lines on Workbook pages 2 and 3. *What has happened to five of the number cards? They have blown off the washing lines in the wind. You will need to work out where each of the cards should go, and complete them with the number, the number name, and a drawing to show how many tens and how many ones.*

Activity
Children work from Workbook pages 2 and 3. They complete the two missing parts of each of the five cards, and then draw a line from each card to show where it should go on the washing lines.

Extra help
A 1–30 number line would provide useful support. Have some linking cubes available for those who need to make the number in tens and units to help them to draw the quantity.

Further extension
Ask children to write the numbers from one to twenty, or beyond if you have time, in words, without looking at their workbook.

If you have time
If enough children have completed the Extra activity, collect the completed number cards, mix them up, and ask the group to work together to put them in order.

Be aware

- It can be quite a large leap to show numbers 20 to 29 using two columns of ten and the appropriate units, even when children appear secure in their understanding to 19.

Outcomes

- I can work out which numbers are missing from a 1–20 number line.
- I can write number names from one to twenty.

Supporting resources

- You could provide a washing line with number cards or other numbered items to peg on the line in order.
- You could read a story involving washing lines, such as *Walter's Windy Washing Line* by Neil Griffiths, ISBN 978-0954535308.

A1: counting in 1s up to 100; counting on and back in 10s; recognising the value of digits in a 'teens' number; comparing two numbers

Summary

Y1 ⭐ A1.2

Purses

Individuals, pairs or groups working independently

Year 1 Challenge Workbook page 4

A purse, or a drawing of a purse; 10p coins; £1 coin (optional); 0–100 number line (optional)

Abacus Evolve objectives

- Count on and back in 10s from a multiple of 10

Framework objectives

- *Derive and recall all pairs of numbers with a total of 10 and addition facts for totals to at least 5; work out the corresponding subtraction facts*

Teacher notes

Preparation
If you don't have a purse to use in the lesson, draw an outline picture of a purse.

Getting started
Practise counting in 10s to 100, as a group.

Show the purse, and put a handful of 10p coins on the table. *Can you put 10p in the purse?* Ask one child to put one 10p coin on the purse. *Can someone else put 40p in the purse?* Ask another child to put four 10p coins on the purse. Encourage children to count along in 10s. Move the four 10p coins to one side, and ask another child to draw the four 10p coins in the purse. If they have trouble drawing the coins, show them how to draw around them.

Activity
Children work from Workbook page 4. They read the label of each purse, then draw the correct number of 10p coins in each. Children should not spend a long time drawing the detail of the coins. A rough circle with *10p* written inside it is fine.

Extra help
A 0–100 number line would provide useful support when counting the 10p coins.

Give children 10p coins to use during the activity so that they can count the correct number of coins into the purse before copying them or drawing around them. This reduces the steps between counting and recording, which will make it easier for some children to keep track of what they are doing.

If you have time
Show children a £1 coin. Explain that this is worth ten 10p coins. Ask a child to count out ten 10p coins, and demonstrate replacing it with the £1 coin. Show children the £ symbol, and give them a chance to try writing it.

Be aware

- Real coins can be dirty. Either wash them first or ask children to wash their hands after handling them. Alternatively, use plastic coins (though it is better to use real coins if possible).

Outcomes

- I can count in 10s to 100.
- I can draw 10p coins to match an amount in pence.

Challenge Plan: Year 1

A1: counting in 1s up to 100; counting on and back in 10s; recognising the value of digits in a 'teens' number; comparing two numbers

Summary

Y1 ⭐ A1.3

Finders keepers

Groups working independently

Year 1 Challenge PCM 1

6-sided dice with sides labelled 1, 2, 3; sticky labels; mini whiteboard and pen; around twenty 10p coins; counters; 0–100 number line (optional); £1 coin (optional)

Abacus Evolve objectives

- Count on and back in 10s from a multiple of 10
- Recognise coins of different values
- Find totals of sets of coins

Framework objectives

- *Derive and recall all pairs of numbers with a total of 10 and addition facts for totals to at least 5; work out the corresponding subtraction facts*
- Solve problems involving counting, adding, subtracting, doubling or halving in the context of numbers, measures or money, for example to 'pay' and 'give change'
- Listen to and follow instructions accurately, asking for help if necessary

Teacher notes

Preparation
Photocopy PCM 1, enlarged to A3 if possible.
Make a 1, 2, 3 dice by covering the numbers 4, 5 and 6 with sticky labels and writing 1, 2 and 3 on the labels. Collect enough coins and counters for the number of children who are playing.

Getting started
Show children the game board on PCM 1. Place the 10p coins in the 10p bank. Explain how to play the game: *All place your counters on Start. Take turns to roll the dice and move your counter the matching number of spaces. If you land on a picture of a 10p coin, you collect a 10p coin from the bank. If anyone lands on a question mark, everyone must count up how much money they have collected in total. Write your totals on a mini whiteboard. You only have to do this the first time someone lands on a question mark. Stop the game when someone lands on or passes Finish. At the end of the game, all count up your money again and write your totals on the mini whiteboard. The person with the most money is the winner.*

Activity
Children play the game as a group.

Extra help
A 0–100 number line would provide useful support when counting the 10p coins.

If you have time
Ask children to look at the mini whiteboard. *Who had the most/least when you got to each question mark? Did the same person have the most/least at the end of the game?*

Show the children that 100p = £1 and practise writing the £ symbol.

Be aware

- Real coins can be dirty! Either wash them first or ask children to wash their hands after handling them. Alternatively, use plastic coins (though it is better to use real coins if possible).

Outcomes

- I can count in 10s to 100 and beyond.

Challenge Plan: Year 1

A1: counting in 1s up to 100; counting on and back in 10s; recognising the value of digits in a 'teens' number; comparing two numbers

Summary

Y1 ⬠ A1.4

Coin collector

A small group working with an adult

Year 1 Challenge PCM 2

6-sided dice with sides labelled 1, 2, 3; sticky labels; mini whiteboard and pen; around twenty 1p coins; around fifteen 10p coins; counters; 0–100 number line (optional); £1 coin (optional)

Abacus Evolve objectives

- Recognise the value of each digit in a 'teens' number
- Begin to partition 2-digit numbers into T and U
- Recognise coins of different values
- Exchange coins for equivalent in 10p and 1p coins
- Find totals of sets of coins

Framework objectives

- *Read and write numerals from 0 to 20, then beyond; use knowledge of place value to position these numbers on a number track and number line*
- Solve problems involving counting, adding, subtracting, doubling or halving in the context of numbers, measures or money, for example to 'pay' and 'give change'
- Listen to and follow instructions accurately, asking for help and clarification if necessary

Teacher notes

Preparation
Photocopy PCM 2, enlarged to A3 if possible.

Make a 1, 2, 3 dice by covering the numbers 4, 5 and 6 with sticky labels and writing 1, 2 and 3 on the labels. Collect enough coins and counters for the number of children who are playing.

Activity
- Show children the game board on PCM 2. Explain how to play the game.
  - Children play as a group. They each place their counter on Start. They take turns to roll the 1, 2, 3 dice, and move their counter that number of spaces.
  - If they land on a picture of a 1p coin, they collect a real 1p coin. If they land on a picture of a 10p coin, they collect a real 10p coin. If they land on a picture of two coins, they collect the two coins.
  - If a child lands on a star, they can choose whether to collect a 1p coin or a 10p coin, or get rid of a 1p or 10p coin.
  - The aim is to get as close as possible to 50p when they land on or pass Finish.
  - Once a child has collected ten 1p coins, they can swap them for a 10p coin. Explain that this has the same value, and it will make it easier for them to count up their money at the end of the game.
  - When the first child lands on or passes Finish, they wait until the rest of the group have done the same. Then all the children count the money they have collected. The player whose total is closest to 50p wins.
- Children play the game. Encourage them to keep a track of their total as they go, so that if they land on a star they can make a good decision about whether to collect or get rid of a coin.

Extra help
A 0–100 number line would provide useful support when counting the coins.

Further extension
Ask children to compare their collections of coins. *Who has the most money? Who has the least? Which coins would Amla need to collect to get the same total as Ian?* Ask the group to collect all their coins together. *How much money is there in total? Is there a quick way to count it?*

Show the children that 100p = £1 and practise writing the £ symbol.

If you have time
Ask children what they thought of the game. *How could we make it better next time?*

Be aware

- Children often have difficulty switching between counting in 10s and 1s. Scaffold the change by counting with them at that point.

Outcomes

- I can count in 10s and 1s.
- I can find the total of a set of 10p coins and 1p coins.

Challenge Plan: Year 1

A1: counting in 1s up to 100; counting on and back in 10s; recognising the value of digits in a 'teens' number; comparing two numbers

Summary

Y1 ⭐ A1.5	**Parcel post**
	Individuals or pairs working independently
	Year 1 Challenge Workbook page 5
	10p and 1p stamps, or pictures of them; paper; envelopes; boxes; brown paper (all optional)

Abacus Evolve objectives

- Recognise the value of each digit in a 'teens' number
- Begin to partition 2-digit numbers into T and U

Framework objectives

- *Read and write numerals from 0 to 20, then beyond; use knowledge of place value to position these numbers on a number track and number line*

Teacher notes

Getting started
Look at Workbook page 5 together. Point to the picture of the parcel with one 10p and four 1p stamps on it. Point to a 1p stamp. *How much is this worth? How many of these stamps are there? How much are they worth altogether?* Point to a 10p stamp. *How much is this worth? So what is the total value of the five stamps? Why does the parcel not have fourteen 1p stamps on it?* If necessary, explain that 14 stamps would take up a lot of space, so we replace ten of them with one 10p stamp. Make the link to replacing ten 1p coins with one 10p coin.

Activity
Children work from Workbook page 5. Children draw the correct numbers of 10p and 1p stamps on each parcel to match the labels.

Extra help
Give children real or pretend 10p and 1p stamps so that they can count out the correct amount before drawing on the parcels.

Further extension
How many 10p stamps have been used on all the parcels? How many 1p stamps? How much would it cost to buy all the stamps?

If you have time
Set up the role play area as a post office. Draw stamps, or print out pictures of them. Ask children to draw some as well. Provide lots of paper, envelopes, boxes and brown paper.

Be aware

- First and second class stamps for letters do not show their numerical value, so they may not be very useful for this activity. However, you can get stamps with numerical values from post offices for making up parcels.

Outcomes

- I know how many tens and how many ones there are in a 2-digit number.
- I can count out 10p and 1p stamps to match a given value.

Challenge Plan: Year 1

A1: counting in 1s up to 100; counting on and back in 10s; recognising the value of digits in a 'teens' number; comparing two numbers

Summary

Y1 ⭐ A1.6

Biggest, smallest

A small group working with an adult

Year 1 Challenge Workbook page 6

Number cards 0–50; red and blue colouring pencils; 0–50 number line (optional)

Abacus Evolve objectives

- Say which is more or less of two numbers
- Order numbers up to at least 30
- Recognise the value of each digit in a 'teens' number
- Begin to partition 2-digit numbers into T and U

Framework objectives

- Compare and order numbers, using the related vocabulary; use the equals (=) sign
- *Read and write numerals from 0 to 20, then beyond; use knowledge of place value to position these numbers on a number track and number line*
- Describe simple patterns and relationships involving numbers or shapes; decide whether examples satisfy given conditions
- Take turns to speak, listen to others' suggestions and talk about what they are going to do

Teacher notes

Activity

- Show children number cards 8, 6 and 7. Ask one child to put them in order. Ask another child to point to the biggest number, and another to point to the smallest. *How do you know?*
- Repeat with number cards 16, 18, 19 and 17. Encourage discussion about tens and units, and about which digit to look at first.
- Show children Workbook page 6. Look at the first set of three numbers together. Ask children to colour the biggest number in each set red and the smallest blue. Ask them to do the same for the next two sets.
- When everyone has completed the first three sets, look at some of the other sets together. *The numbers are jumbled up to try to trick you. How can you avoid getting tricked?*
- Ask children to complete the Workbook page. As they are working, occasionally ask one of them to explain why they have chosen to colour a particular number red or blue.
- When everyone has finished, ask children to compare their pages, discuss any discrepancies, and come to an agreement about the correct answers.

Extra help

If a child gets stuck on a set of cards, ask them to pick out the number cards to match the set. Ask them to put the cards in order, and identify the largest and smallest numbers. Shuffle the cards and ask the child to find the largest and smallest again. *Have they changed?* They should now be able to colour the appropriate cards on the page.

A 0–50 number line would provide useful support.

Further extension

Shuffle the cards and give each child five cards face down. Ask children to turn over their cards when you say *Go!* The first child to identify the largest and smallest numbers in their set wins. Collect the cards, shuffle well and repeat.

Be aware

- Even if children are very familiar with the order of numbers, some find it difficult to identify the largest and smallest numbers when the sequence is not continuous and the numbers are not in order. If necessary, use a number line for support.

Outcomes

- I can put numbers up to 50 in order.
- I can find the biggest and smallest number in a set.
- I can split numbers into tens and ones.

Challenge Plan: Year 1

B1: saying the number that is 1 more; counting on 1, 2, 3 or 4; addition facts totals up to 6; relating addition facts to an understanding of addition

Summary

Y1 ⬡ B1.1

... And another one

A small group working with an adult

1–100 number line or 1–100 square; number cards 1–100 (optional)

Abacus Evolve objectives	Framework objectives
• Say the number that is 1 more than a given number	• Say the number that is 1 more or less than any given number and 10 more or less for multiples of 10 • Describe simple patterns and relationships involving numbers or shapes; decide whether examples satisfy given conditions • Listen with sustained concentration

Teacher notes

Preparation
Draw a picture of a boy, 'Ben', on the board, with a speech bubble saying: '*I can always think of a number 1 bigger than your number.*'

Activity
- Organise the group sitting in a circle. Make sure a 1–100 square or a 1–100 number line is visible.
- Say a number less than 20, e.g. *8*. Ask the child to your left to say the number 1 more. Ask the next child to say a different number less than 20. Ask the child to their left to say the number 1 more. Continue like this around the group, making sure that each child has a turn to say the number 1 more.
- *Who can tell me the number that is 1 bigger than 100? Let's keep adding 1 more and see if we get stuck.* Repeat with different starting numbers larger than 100 to see if children can say the next number.
- *What is the biggest number you can think of? Can anyone tell me the number which is 1 more than that? How did you work it out?*
- Point to your picture of Ben. *Ben thinks that it is always possible to think of a number bigger than one that someone else says. Is he right? Why do you think that? In pairs, challenge each other to find a number that is one bigger than the one your partner says.* Give children a chance to try this out. *Will the game ever end?*

Extra help
Use numbers that are smaller to suit the needs of the group. Encourage children to make up their own names for consecutive numbers, to help them to remember what they are, for example 'follow on' numbers or 'one more' numbers.

Further extension
Introduce the concept of infinity and ask children to discuss it. Ask children to interview each other as if they were on the news trying to explain to the audience what infinity is. One child in each pair is the interviewer and one is the explainer.

If you have time
Lay a trail of consecutive number cards around the playground. Children start at a given number and collect all the available numbers in order to make their own collection of consecutive numbers.

Be aware	Outcomes
• Many children are fascinated by large numbers, for example millions and hundreds of millions. They will hear references to large numbers on the news, on advertising and in computer technologies. Inviting children to collect large numbers can open a dialogue about the relative size of these numbers.	• I can say the number names in order. • I can say the number 1 more than any number up to 100, and beyond. • I know that by adding 1 more I can find the next number in the counting sequence.

Supporting resources

Create strings of consecutive numbers using this online maths dictionary (click on 'C', then 'consecutive'):
- http://www.teachers.ash.org.au/jeather/maths/dictionary.html

Challenge Plan: Year 1

B1: saying the number that is 1 more; counting on 1, 2, 3 or 4; addition facts totals up to 6; relating addition facts to an understanding of addition

Summary

Y1 ⭐ B1.2 **Hop, skip and jump**

Pairs or groups working independently

Year 1 Challenge Workbook page 7

Abacus Evolve objectives

- Relate counting on to addition and to addition sentences
- Begin to recognise that addition can be done in any order
- Add by counting on, not bridging a multiple of 10 other than 10 or 20
- Begin to recognise that more than two numbers can be added together
- Begin to use the + and = signs to record addition sentences
- Relate addition facts for pairs of numbers to an understanding of addition, including use of + and =

Framework objectives

- Relate addition to counting on; recognise that addition can be done in any order; use practical and informal written methods to support the addition of a 1-digit number or a multiple of 10 to a 1-digit or 2-digit number
- *Use the vocabulary related to addition and subtraction and symbols to describe and record addition and subtraction number sentences*
- Solve problems involving counting, adding, subtracting, doubling or halving in the context of numbers, measures or money, for example to 'pay' and 'give change'

Teacher notes

Getting started
Show children Workbook page 7. *It is sports day, and these three children are taking part in the jumping competition!* Explain the rules of the competition: each child must do three jumps. They can choose from hops, skips or jumps. Children will need to work out each child's score.

You will need to add sets of three scores – one score for each jump. What is a quick way to add three small numbers? Are there any numbers that are easy to add together?

Activity
Children work from Workbook page 7. They work out the scores for each child's jumps, then work out each child's total score. From these totals, they work out which child is the winner. They record their additions, totals and the winner's name in the table.

Extra help
Change the rules so that instead of choosing three ways to jump, children have to choose two ways. For example, one jump and one skip would give a total of 7 points.

Further extension
If Chen had scored 10 points, what types of jumps might he have chosen? How many options are there?

Now try to find all the different ways of scoring 10 points, if you can make any number of jumps.

If you have time
Create your own jumping game and make up your own values for hops, skips and jumps. Who is the winner?

Be aware

- Adding three small numbers efficiently may be a challenge. Encourage children to look for pairs that total 10, or doubles, and to start with the larger number and count on the smaller numbers.

Outcomes

- I can add three small numbers.
- I can use + and = to record number sentences.

Challenge Plan: Year 1

B1: saying the number that is 1 more; counting on 1, 2, 3 or 4; addition facts totals up to 6; relating addition facts to an understanding of addition

Summary

Y1 ⭐ B1.3

Cube scores

Individuals, pairs or groups working independently

Year 1 Challenge Workbook page 8

Red, blue and yellow linking cubes; 6-sided dice; 1 minute sand-timer (optional); green cubes (optional)

Abacus Evolve objectives

- Relate counting on to addition and to addition sentences
- Begin to recognise that addition can be done in any order
- Add by counting on, not bridging a multiple of 10 other than 10 or 20
- Begin to recognise that more than two numbers can be added together
- Begin to use the + and = signs to record addition sentences
- Relate addition facts for pairs of numbers to an understanding of addition, including use of + and =

Framework objectives

- Relate addition to counting on; recognise that addition can be done in any order; use practical and informal written methods to support the addition of a 1-digit number or a multiple of 10 to a 1-digit or 2-digit number
- *Use the vocabulary related to addition and subtraction and symbols to describe and record addition and subtraction number sentences*
- Describe simple patterns and relationships involving numbers or shapes; decide whether examples satisfy given conditions

Teacher notes

Getting started
Show children Workbook page 8, and give them lots of red, blue and yellow cubes. Make sure they understand the value of each of the cubes, and how to play the game. The focus of this activity should be on developing systematic ways of recording. Ask children to think about a system they could use before they start the game.

Activity
Children work from Workbook page 8. They throw two dice and find the total. They then find all the possible ways to make that total using any three cubes. Children play three times.

Children could also play this game in groups of three or more. Player A throws the dice and finds the total. If the total cannot be made, Player A throws the dice again. Players B and C then have 1 minute to each find as many different ways as possible to make the total. Player A times them with a 1-minute sand-timer. After the minute is up, Player A checks Player B's and Player C's additions, and awards points according to the number of correct ways. Children record their scores, then swap roles. They play three times, so that each child has a chance to be the timer. After three rounds, they compare scores.

Extra help
Give children just red and blue cubes, and one dice. For example, a child might throw a 5, and there is only one way to make the total: 2 + 3 (or two ways, if you allow children to count 3 + 2 as a separate option).

Are there any totals that cannot be made?

Further extension
Allow children to use any number of cubes in their search for all the possible ways to make a given total. *How does this affect the number of different ways of making the total? Repeat the game to work out what is happening.*

If you have time
Ask children to make the same three totals, but this time they can use a green cube as well, worth 1 point. *What happens to the number of different ways now? Can you think of a systematic way of recording these options?*

Be aware

- Some children may be able to make generalisations and look for patterns, for example increasing the number of cubes increases the number of ways of making the total.

Outcomes

- I can add three small numbers.
- I can use + and = to record number sentences.
- I can use a system to find all the possibilities.

Challenge Plan: Year 1

B1: saying the number that is 1 more; counting on 1, 2, 3 or 4; addition facts totals up to 6; relating addition facts to an understanding of addition

Summary

Y1 ⭐ B1.4

Round and round

Groups working independently

Year 1 Challenge PCM 3

1p coins; bags; 1–6 dice; sticky labels (optional); 1–9 dice (optional)

Abacus Evolve objectives

- Recognise a number of objects up to 6 without counting
- Know by heart addition facts for pairs of numbers that total up to 6
- Add by counting on, not bridging a multiple of 10 other than 10 or 20

Framework objectives

- Count reliably at least 20 objects, recognising that when rearranged the number of objects stays the same; estimate a number of objects that can be checked by counting
- *Derive and recall all pairs of numbers with a total of 10 and addition facts for totals to at least 5; work out the corresponding subtraction facts*
- Ask and answer questions, make relevant contributions, offer suggestions and take turns

Teacher notes

Preparation
Photocopy PCM 3. Prepare bags of six 1p coins (one bag per child).

Getting started
Give each child a bag with six 1p coins in it, and sit them in a circle. Ask children to write their names in the table on PCM 3. *How much money do you each have?* Ask each child to record their amount in the table. *How much money do you have altogether?* Ask one child to record the total amount of money.

If possible, demonstrate how to play the game by playing one round with the group. Ask a child to throw a dice. They take that number of 1p coins from their bag, and pass them to the child on their left. That child throws the dice and does the same. Children continue until they have all had a turn. *How much money do you each have now? Do you know without looking in your bag?* Ask each child to record their new amount. *How much money do you have altogether?* Children should realise that the total number of coins is still the same. *You are going to play three more rounds. You should try to keep track of how many coins you have, and only count them to check.*

Activity
Children work from PCM 3, and play the game as a group.

Extra help
Children can use a 1–3 dice instead of a 1–6 dice. Cover 4, 5 and 6 with stickers and draw on one dot, two dots and three dots.

Further extension
Children can use a 1–9 dice, and start with 9p each.

Be aware

- Observing which children understand the conservation of money in this game is useful as this indicates which children understand that, although individuals have lost or gained money, the group as a whole has the same amount of money throughout.

Outcomes

- I can add and subtract small amounts to and from a starting amount, and know the new total without counting.

Supporting resources

Show children a short animation about counting and adding within the context of money (search for clip 1919):
- http://www.bbc.co.uk/learningzone/clips/

Challenge Plan: Year 1

Summary

Y1 ⬡ **B1.5**   **Six in a line**

A small group working with an adult

Year 1 Challenge PCMs 4 and 5

Coloured pencils; paper; 1 minute sand-timer

Abacus Evolve objectives

- Begin to know by heart addition facts for pairs of numbers that total up to 7
- Relate number bonds to an understanding of addition, including use of +, −, =
- Record addition and subtraction facts for pairs of numbers that total up to 9, using +, − and = in number sentences

Framework objectives

- *Derive and recall all pairs of numbers with a total of 10 and addition facts for totals to at least 5; work out the corresponding subtraction facts*
- *Use the vocabulary related to addition and subtraction and symbols to describe and record addition and subtraction number sentences*
- *Listen with sustained concentration*

Teacher notes

Preparation
Photocopy PCMs 4 and 5. Cut out the bingo grids on PCM 5.

Activity
- Give each child a bingo grid from PCM 5, a coloured pencil and a sheet of paper.
- *I am going to read out questions, and you will have 60 seconds to work out each answer before I move on to the next question. If the answer to a question is 6, you can colour one of the number 6s on your grid. You must also write the matching addition or subtraction on your sheet of paper. Your aim is to colour six 6s in a line.*
  The line can be horizontal, vertical or diagonal. If you get six 6s in a line, you say 'Bingo!'
- Play one round, with you reading the questions on PCM 4 and using a sand-timer to time a 1 minute gap between each question.
- After a child has got six 6s in a line, ask children to compare the additions and subtractions they have written down. *Have you all written the same things?* Point to particular calculations and ask children to explain how they worked them out.
- Ask children to work as a group to create their own similar bingo game. They can choose a new target number between 5 and 9, create a few grids of numbers, and write their own questions.
  If there is time, children can play their game as a group, with one child as the caller.

Extra help
Give children PCM 4. Ask them to sort out which questions they think are easy and which ones they think are difficult. Discuss what they think makes them difficult. *How could you change them to make them easier?* Ask children to re-write some of the questions. *Can you work out the answers now? What made them easier?*

Further extension
Ask children to work in threes. They each write at least five additions and subtractions. They pass these to the next child, who turns each of them into a word problem. For example, 4 + 6 could be changed to '*I had four sweets, then my mum gave me six more. How many do I have now?*' Children then pass the word problems to the next child, and each child solves the word problems they have been given.

Be aware

- Reassure children that this is not a test situation and if they miss a question it may not matter. Keeping calm and waiting for the next question is a great skill for mental maths tests.

Outcomes

- I can solve simple addition and subtraction questions.
- I can find different calculations with the answer 6.

Challenge Plan: Year 1

B1: saying the number that is 1 more; counting on 1, 2, 3 or 4; addition facts totals up to 6; relating addition facts to an understanding of addition

Summary

Y1 ⭐ B1.6

Totals of 7

Individuals, pairs or groups working independently

Year 1 Challenge Workbook page 9

Number cards 0–7 (optional)

Abacus Evolve objectives

- Begin to know by heart addition facts for pairs of numbers that total up to 7
- Begin to use the + and = signs to record addition sentences
- Relate addition facts for pairs of numbers to an understanding of addition, including use of + and =

Framework objectives

- *Derive and recall all pairs of numbers with a total of 10 and addition facts for totals to at least 5; work out the corresponding subtraction facts*
- *Use the vocabulary related to addition and subtraction and symbols to describe and record addition and subtraction number sentences*
- *Describe simple patterns and relationships involving numbers or shapes; decide whether examples satisfy given conditions*

Teacher notes

Getting started
Show children Workbook page 9. Explain that they will be looking for different ways to make a total of 7, using the numbers in the two bags.

Activity
Children work from Workbook page 9. They investigate the number of ways they can make a total of 7 by adding pairs of numbers 0–7. Encourage them to come up with their own system to make sure they find all the possibilities.

They then try to find all the ways of making 7 if they can only use each number once. They should think about what effect this has on the number of different ways.

Extra help
Ask children to do the activity, but imagine that they have numbers 0–7 in one bag, and 0–3 in the other. Give children number cards so they can pair them up physically.

Further extension
Ask children to do the activity, but imagine that they have numbers 0–9 in each bag. *How many different ways are there now? Why is that? What happens to the number of possibilities if you increase the number of numbers?*

If you have time
Ask children to investigate the number of ways to make 8, using numbers 0–8. Then ask them to try making 9, using numbers 0–9. *Do you notice any patterns?*

Information
Children should find eight ways to make 7 using the digits 0–7.
0 + 7   1 + 6   2 + 5   3 + 4   4 + 3   5 + 2   6 + 1   7 + 0
If they can only use each number once, there are half as many possibilities.
0 + 7   1 + 6   2 + 5   3 + 4

Be aware

- Creating and using number sentences to explain the meaning of 7 helps to reinforce an understanding of the quantity that the number 7 represents.

Outcomes

- I can find different ways to add two numbers to make 7.
- I can use a system to find all the possibilities.

Supporting resources

This activity involves adding pairs of numbers (tens and units) to make given totals:
- http://nrich.maths.org/public/viewer.php?obj_id=229

Challenge Plan: Year 1

C1: comparing lengths; measuring lengths using non-standard units; days of the week and familiar events; seasons and months

Summary

Y1 ⭐ C1.1

Spiral worms

Individuals, pairs or groups working independently

Year 1 Challenge PCM 6

String; scissors; sticky labels (optional); a collection of objects with different circumferences (optional)

Abacus Evolve objectives

- Compare two or more lengths or heights by direct comparison

Framework objectives

- *Estimate, measure, weigh and compare objects choosing and using suitable uniform non-standard or standard units and measuring instruments (e.g. a lever balance, metre stick or measuring jug)*
- Describe a puzzle or problem using numbers, practical materials and diagrams; use these to solve the problem and set the solution in the original context

Teacher notes

Preparation
Photocopy PCM 6, one copy per child.
Dampen the string to make it easier to handle.

Getting started
Show children PCM 6 and demonstrate how to use the string to measure the worms, including marking and cutting the string.

Activity
Children work from PCM 6. They see pictures of four coiled worms, and are given information about the relative lengths of the worms. They lay string along the worms, mark the ends and cut off any extra string. They discard any unwanted pieces and keep those that are the same length as each worm. Then chidren compare the lengths of string and decide which worm is which. They write the correct names below the worms.

Further extension
Challenge the children to find curved 3D objects which measure the same length around as each spiral worm.

If you have time
Children can compare their measurements and share ideas about where to look for items with the same circumference.

Be aware

- Some children may find it difficult to keep track of which string represents which worm. Give them some sticky labels to fold over the string and label if necessary.

Outcomes

- I can measure curved objects with string.
- I can compare and order lengths.

Supporting resources

- Have a collection of measuring devices for children to explore.

Challenge Plan: Year 1

C1: comparing lengths; measuring lengths using non-standard units; days of the week and familiar events; seasons and months

Summary

Y1 ✩ C1.2

Measuring in hands

Individuals, pairs or groups working independently

Year 1 Challenge Workbook page 10

Roll of paper (optional); fabric (optional); pencils or pens (optional).

Abacus Evolve objectives

- Estimate then measure lengths, recording estimates
- Measure lengths using uniform non-standard units (whole, half and quarter)

Framework objectives

- *Estimate, measure, weigh and compare objects choosing and using suitable uniform non-standard or standard units and measuring instruments (e.g. a lever balance, metre stick or measuring jug)*
- Describe a puzzle or problem using numbers, practical materials and diagrams; use these to solve the problem and set the solution in the original context

Teacher notes

Preparation
Have a roll of paper available for children to lie down on to mark and measure themselves.
Measure a piece of fabric 10 hands long. Use your own (adult) hands.

Getting started
Show Workbook page 10 and explain what to do. Ensure the children are aware of which way up to use their hands.

Activity
Children work from Workbook page 10. They find objects like the ones in the picture and estimate, then measure, the heights of the objects in hands. They compare their measurements with other children in the group and talk about why their answers may not all be the same.

Further extension
Challenge each child to find a way to measure their own height with their own hands. If necessary, suggest they work with a partner. One child could lie down on paper while their partner marks where the top of their head and heels reach. The child can then measure themselves using their own hands.

If you have time
Give children the piece of fabric labelled '10 hands' and ask them to check it has been labelled correctly. Challenge them to work out what the problem is. Encourage children to talk about what the problems are by using part of your body to measure. Ask them to suggest units of measurement that would be better.

Be aware

- If children's measurements are rather different than might be expected, check that they used their hands in the correct orientation.

Outcomes

- I can measure the height of objects in hands.

Supporting resources

These websites give more information about measuring horses in hands:
- http://www.cowgirl.net/content/HowtoMeasureaHorse.pdf
- http://www.cowboyway.com/HowTo/HorseHeight.htm
- http://www.horseracinghistory.co.uk/hrho/jsp/education/measure.jsp

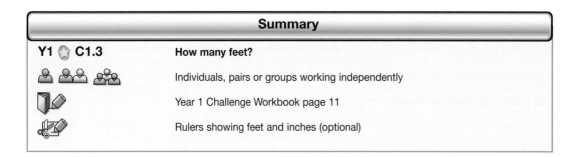

Challenge Plan: Year 1

C1: comparing lengths; measuring lengths using non-standard units; days of the week and familiar events; seasons and months

Summary

Y1 ☆ C1.3

How many feet?

Individuals, pairs or groups working independently

Year 1 Challenge Workbook page 11

Rulers showing feet and inches (optional)

Abacus Evolve objectives

- Estimate then measure lengths, recording estimates
- Measure lengths using uniform non-standard units (whole, half and quarter)

Framework objectives

- *Estimate, measure, weigh and compare objects choosing and using suitable uniform non-standard or standard units and measuring instruments (e.g. a lever balance, metre stick or measuring jug)*
- Describe a puzzle or problem using numbers, practical materials and diagrams; use these to solve the problem and set the solution in the original context
- Take turns to speak, listen to others' suggestions and talk about what they are going to do.

Teacher notes

Preparation
Decide whether you want children to work with or without their shoes on.

Getting started
Show Workbook page 11 and explain what to do. Ensure children are aware that the heel of one foot must just touch the toes of the other.

Activity
Children work from Workbook page 11. They estimate the width and length of their own classroom then measure it using their own feet. They compare their measurements with a partner and discuss why they are the same or different. Encourage children to talk about what the problems are with using part of your body to measure. Ask them to suggest units of measurement that would be better.

Extra help
Children could work in pairs, with one offering physical support to the other as they measure by moving heel to toe across the room.

If you have time
Ask children to estimate, then measure in feet, how far to the cloakroom, to the toilet or other places they regularly go to from the classroom.

Be aware

- Some children find it hard to balance when walking heel to toe. Ensure that some measures can be taken where there is support, for example along a wall. Give children time to practise, for example as a cool down activity in PE.

Outcomes

- I can measure the length of objects in feet.

Supporting resources

- Provide a selection of tape measures and rulers marked in feet and inches.

Challenge Plan: Year 1

C1: comparing lengths; measuring lengths using non-standard units; days of the week and familiar events; seasons and months

Summary

Y1 ☆ C1.4

Days of the week

Pairs working independently

Year 1 Challenge Workbook page 12

Year 1 Challenge PCM 7

Scissors; cloth bag; laminator (optional); coloured beads (optional); thread (optional)

Abacus Evolve objectives

- **Y2** Use units of time and know the relationship between them: hours in a day, days in a week

Framework objectives

- **Y2** *Use units of time (seconds, minutes, hours, days) and know the relationships between them; read the time to the quarter hour; identify time intervals, including those that cross the hour*

Teacher notes

Preparation
Photocopy PCM 7, one copy per pair. Cut out the cards. If possible, laminate the PCMs before cutting out the cards.

Getting started
Give each pair of children a cloth bag, and put two sets of day of the week cards into it. Explain how to play the game.

Activity
Children work from Workbook page 12. They play the days of the week ladder game. The two players take turns to take a card from their bag and put it on their time ladder. The first card must be placed at the top of the ladder. When subsequent cards are chosen, children must work out which spaces they should go in, if they are to end up with all the days in order. Duplicate cards must be returned to the bag and the player misses that turn. The winner is the first player to complete the whole week. When the ladder is complete, children can copy the days of the week onto the ladder on Workbook page 12 and add an illustration for each day.

Extra help
Remind children of a days-of-the-week song to help them put the days in the correct order.
Children can make a days-of-the-week bracelet. For each day of the week, choose a bead in a colour that starts with the same letter as the day of the week (for example Monday = maroon; Tuesday and Thursday = turquoise; Wednesday = white; Friday = fuchsia; Saturday and Sunday = silver). They thread the beads in the correct order and tie it to make a bracelet. Children can then use the bracelet to help them recite the days of the week in order from any starting point.

If you have time
Encourage children to tell you or another child what each day makes them think of.

Be aware

- Children might think they have to wait until they find the 'Monday' card in order to start the game. Remind children that the days of the week are a continuous cycle.

Outcomes

- I can order the days of the week, starting with any day.

Supporting resources

- Provide a selection of diaries and calendars.

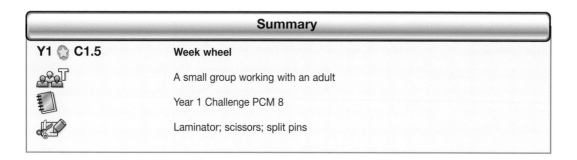

Challenge Plan: Year 1

C1: comparing lengths; measuring lengths using non-standard units; days of the week and familiar events; seasons and months

---

Summary

Y1 ⬡ C1.5

Week wheel

A small group working with an adult

Year 1 Challenge PCM 8

Laminator; scissors; split pins

Abacus Evolve objectives

- **Y2** Use units of time and know the relationship between them: hours in a day, days in a week

Framework objectives

- **Y2** *Use units of time (seconds, minutes, hours, days) and know the relationships between them; read the time to the quarter hour; identify time intervals, including those that cross the hour*

Teacher notes

Preparation
Photocopy PCM 8, one copy per child. Laminate the sheets and then cut out the week wheels and the pointers. Use the split pin to attach the pointer to the week wheel.

Getting started
Make sure the pointer rotates freely. Ask children to recite the days of the week as they turn the pointer.

Activity
- Ask children to use the week wheel to answer these questions.
  - *Which day is two days after Monday?*
  - *Which day is three days after Friday?*
  - *How many days between Tuesday and Saturday?*
  - *Which day is four days after Sunday?*
- Ask each child to make up one or more questions like these. They then take turns to answer each other's questions, using the wheel to check the answers are correct.

Further extension
Children can give a fact about each day. *When do we go to the library? Which days do we have PE? Which day do you go swimming?* They can discuss how regularly events happen (more than once a week, once a week, once a fortnight, once a month, once a year).

If you have time
Challenge children to recite the days of the week starting from a day other than Monday.

Be aware

- Children may find it difficult to recognise that the order of the days simply repeats itself. Use a diary to show they are repeated again and again.

Outcomes

- I can use the order of the days of the week to answer questions.

Supporting resources

- Provide a selection of diaries and calendars.

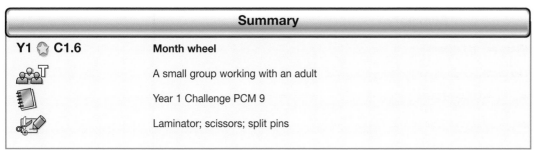

Challenge Plan: Year 1

C1: comparing lengths; measuring lengths using non-standard units; days of the week and familiar events; seasons and months

Summary

Y1 ⭐ C1.6

Month wheel

A small group working with an adult

Year 1 Challenge PCM 9

Laminator; scissors; split pins

Abacus Evolve objectives

- **Y2** Use units of time and know the relationship between them: months in a year, seasons in a year
- **Y2** Order the months of the year

Framework objectives

- **Y2** *Use units of time (seconds, minutes, hours, days) and know the relationships between them; read the time to the quarter hour; identify time intervals, including those that cross the hour*

Teacher notes

Preparation
Photocopy PCM 9, one copy per child. Laminate the sheets and then cut out the month wheels and the pointers. Use the split pin to attach the pointer to the month wheel.

Activity
- Make sure the pointer rotates freely. Ask children to recite the months of the year as they turn the pointer.
- Ask children to use the month wheel to answer these questions.
  - *Which month is two months after January?*
  - *Which month is three months after July?*
  - *Which month is three months before September?*
- Ask each child to make up one or more questions like these. They then take turns to answer each other's questions, using the wheel to check the answers are correct.

Further extension
Children discuss the particular features of each month. *Is it your birthday? A friend's birthday? A special time of the year?* Together discuss the changing of seasons.

If you have time
Encourage children to practise until they can recite the months of the year in order. Challenge them to start from a month other than January.

Be aware

- Children may find it difficult to recognise that the months repeat themselves over and over. Collect calendars to show that the year number changes but there are always the same 12 months in the same order. Relate understanding to your work in history activities.

Outcomes

- I can use the order of the months of the year to answer questions.

Supporting resources

- Provide a selection of calendars.

Challenge Plan: Year 1

D1: names of common 2D shapes; features of familiar 2D shapes; counting back 1; subtracting a 1-digit number from a 'teens' number

Summary

Y1 ⭐ D1.1

Where are the shapes?

Pairs working independently

Year 1 Challenge Workbook page 13

Year 1 Challenge PCMs 10, 11 and 12

Card or paper in three different colours; scissors; plastic or wooden rectangles and squares in three different colours (optional); digital camera (optional); magazines (optional)

Abacus Evolve objectives

- Begin to use the names of common 2D shapes: circle, square, rectangle, triangle

Framework objectives

- *Visualise and name common 2D shapes and 3D solids and describe their features; use them to make patterns, pictures and models*

Teacher notes

Preparation
Photocopy PCM 12 on to three different coloured sheets of card or paper and cut shapes out. Alternatively, you could use plastic or wooden rectangles and squares in three different colours.
Photocopy PCM 11. Cut out the labels and fold the 'rectangle' and 'square' labels so they stand up. (You will not need the 'triangle' and 'circle' labels for this activity).
For each child who may get to the Extra activity on the Workbook page, make a few photocopies of PCM 10.

Getting started
Show children the shapes and labels. Make sure they can read the words 'rectangle', 'square', 'why' and 'because'. Explain to the children that they will be working in pairs because you want them to listen to each other and share their ideas by using the 'why?' and 'because...' cards. Explain the activity to the children.

Activity
Children set out the 'square' and 'rectangle' labels. They take turns to choose a shape and put it next to the correct label. Each time a child places a shape, their partner asks them *why* the shape belongs there, and the child must answer starting with *because*.

Children then work from Workbook page 13. They look at a photo of a building and count the number of rectangles and squares. They then compare their totals with a partner and work together to resolve any differences using the 'Why?' and 'Because...' cards.

Extra help
What does a square/rectangle look like upside down? On its side? Sitting on a corner?

If you have time
Make up a story about Mr and Mrs Square. What do you think their house would look like? What about their garden? Can you draw them and explain why you think Mr and Mrs Square would like these things?·

Give children a digital camera and ask them to take photos of rectangles in the room. They can then print the pictures, cut out the rectangles and make a page of rectangles on PCM 10.

Be aware

- Children can find the orientation of shapes a complex concept and therefore might find it challenging to recognise that a diamond shape can also be a square and that a rectangle can be sitting on one corner.

Outcomes

- I can sort shapes into groups and explain my reasons.
- I can recognise shapes in the real world.

Supporting resources

Children can watch 'The Number Crew – Shape Sorting' from Teachers TV to find out more about shapes:
- http://www.teachers.tv/video/1766

Challenge Plan: Year 1

D1: names of common 2D shapes; features of familiar 2D shapes; counting back 1; subtracting a 1-digit number from a 'teens' number

Summary

Y1 ⬠ D1.2

What's my picture?

A group working with an adult

Year 1 Challenge PCMs 12, 13 and 14

Paper or card in four different colours; scissors; magnetic shapes and board or fuzzy felt (optional); individual whiteboards (optional)

Abacus Evolve objectives

- Describe features of familiar 2D shapes: number of sides and corners, types of sides

Framework objectives

- *Visualise and name common 2D shapes and 3D solids and describe their features; use them to make patterns, pictures and models*
- *Experiment with and build new stores of words to communicate in different contexts*

Teacher notes

Preparation

Photocopy PCM 14 once.
Photocopy PCMs 12 and 13 four times each onto coloured paper, then cut out the required shapes. The remaining shapes can be used in the Extra help and Further extension sections. You need two identical sets of 2D shapes: two circles (one red, one yellow), two rectangles (one blue, one green), two squares (one red, one blue) and three triangles (one yellow isosceles, two green right-angled). Make sure children have the correct shapes to make the template on PCM 14.

Activity

- Arrange children into two groups. Give each group the coloured shapes. Give Group 1 the template from PCM 14. Make sure the groups are sitting so that they cannot see the other's shapes or template, for example with an upright book as a barrier between them.
- Group 1 makes a picture by placing coloured shapes onto the template on PCM 14. Group 2 does not look. Group 1 describes their picture. Group 2 makes a replica. They can ask questions about shapes but should not point! The barrier is removed and players discuss whether or not their pictures match. *If they are different, what is different about them?*

Extra help

Remove the barrier and let children work together to make pictures that are the same or different. Give instructions such as: *Tell me three things that are the same in your pictures and one thing that is different.* Use shapes of the same colour to reduce the number of variables.

Further extension

Play the game again but without the template. Player 1 makes a shape picture and describes it. Player 2 tries to make it. Children can make a record of their picture, for example by drawing it, before swapping and beginning again.

If you have time

Children sit back-to-back in pairs on the carpet. Player 1 makes a picture from shapes on a magnetic board (or fuzzy felt). Player 1 draws their picture onto Player 2's back with their finger. Player 2 draws it on a whiteboard. Compare pictures. *What is the same? What is different?* Players swap roles and repeat.

Be aware

- When facing each other, children may find it difficult to describe the position of shapes – left on one picture is right on the other. Use the template to structure the position of the shapes using everyday language, for example the triangle is his hat, it goes on top.

Outcomes

- I can describe the properties of shapes.
- I can explain where to put shapes in a picture.

Supporting resources

Children can also use an online picture maker like this:
- http://www.myfreecolouringpages.com/online_fuzzy_felt.htm

Challenge Plan: Year 1

D1: names of common 2D shapes; features of familiar 2D shapes; counting back 1; subtracting a 1-digit number from a 'teens' number

Summary

Y1 ⬡ D1.3

Shape families

A group working independently

Year 1 Challenge PCMs 15, 16 and 17

Scissors; coloured paper or card (optional)

Abacus Evolve objectives

- Describe the features of familiar 2D shapes: number of sides and corners, types of sides

Framework objectives

- *Visualise and name common 2D shapes and 3D solids and describe their features; use them to make patterns, pictures and models*
- Describe ways of solving puzzles and problems, explaining choices and decisions orally or using pictures
- Ask and answer questions, make relevant contributions, offer suggestions

Teacher notes

Preparation
Photocopy PCMs 15, 16 and 17, one copy of each per child. Cut out the labels and fold the 'quadrilaterals', 'rectangles', 'triangles', 'shapes with a curved side' and 'shapes with more than 4 sides' labels so that they stand up. You will not need the other labels for this activity. Cut out the shapes.

Getting started
Give children the sets of cards. *What do you know about these shapes?* Children use the labels from PCM 17 to sort the shapes into groups. Agree the groups together.

Activity
Each child secretly chooses a group of shape cards and remembers which cards are in their group. Children may choose the same group. Each child keeps one card from their group. One child shuffles the rest of the cards and places them face down in a pile. Children take turns to turn over a card from the pile and add it to their 'shape family' if they can. They tell the rest of the group why it belongs to their shape family. If it doesn't belong to their shape family, another player can claim it. If it doesn't belong to anyone's family, play passes to the next player. If a child gets three cards for their set but cannot complete it (another player may have the card they want), then they can use a wild card. These can be used as any shape.

Extra help
Children play the game with just one set of shape cards from PCM 15. Each child chooses a different group of shapes. Children can then focus on the properties of each shape and explaining why it belongs in their group.

Further extension
Children make up their own set of shape families cards. *Which shapes will you choose? Why?*

Be aware

- The important skill is seeing similarities between the shapes. Children should justify why they have chosen a shape, even if they do not use a mathematical description. As the shapes are grey, children have to use properties other than colour to describe the common features of their shape family.

Outcomes

- I can listen to others and ask them questions about their choices.
- I can talk about shapes.

Supporting resources

Children can try these NRICH activities:
- 'Matching triangles': http://nrich.maths.org/public/viewer.php?obj_id=5638
- 'Making Maths' – Happy Families: http://nrich.maths.org/public/viewer.php?obj_id=5363

D1: names of common 2D shapes; features of familiar 2D shapes; counting back 1; subtracting a 1-digit number from a 'teens' number

Summary

Y1 ⬡ D1.4 Caterpillars

A group of six children working with an adult

Circles and squares of paper; scissors

Abacus Evolve objectives	Framework objectives
• **Y2** Count back in 1s, not crossing a multiple of 10	• **Y2** *Add or subtract mentally a 1-digit number or a multiple of 10 to or from any 2-digit number; use practical and informal written methods to add and subtract 2-digit numbers* • **Y2** Listen to others in class, ask relevant questions and follow instructions

Teacher notes

Preparation
Cut out up to 10 circles of paper per pair, all the same size but any colour. Cut out squares of paper a similar size to the circles, one per child. Write the words *segment* and *caterpillar* on flash cards or a whiteboard.
Display the numbers 1–20 (and higher numbers if appropriate).

Activity
• *We are going to make caterpillars!* Give each pair a square. *This is the caterpillar's head. Draw on eyes and antenna.* Explain that in this caterpillar the segments are made from circles.
• Ask each pair to write a number less than 10 on their square. *The rule is that each segment has a number on it that is 1 less than the segment before. The last segment must have the number 1 on it.*
• Demonstrate starting with 10. *Where is the head? How many segments are there?* Explain that the head does not count as a segment.
• Ask each pair to predict how many circles they will need to complete their caterpillar.
• Pairs complete their caterpillars and check the number of segments. Encourage them to explain how to predict the number of segments. For example, *the number of segments is one less than the number you started with on the head.*
• *What if you had 13 on the head of your caterpillar? How many segments would it have? Work with your partner to decide. Draw a caterpillar to explain how you know your answer.* Pairs explain to the rest of the group how they know the answer. Encourage them to make a statement in words then make a number sentence to explain their idea. Repeat with higher numbers if appropriate.

Extra help
Continue to work on numbers less than 10 if children are not confident in moving onto higher numbers.

Further extension
Start with 100. Pairs explain in words how many segments there will be. *Write that as a number sentence.*
How many segments would there be if 1000 was on the head? Look for a statement that explains the pattern in the segments. For example, *if it was a 1000 caterpillar then there would be 1 less than 1000 segments.*

If you have time
Look at the first caterpillar that the children made. *If each segment had one pair of legs on it, how many legs would the caterpillar have? What if there were two pairs of legs on each segment?* Discuss centipede and millipede legs. Make a centipede display by adding legs to the caterpillars.

Be aware	Outcomes
• Linking words with diagrams is key in using and applying maths. Using clear statements to express a pattern is as important as knowing the answer.	• I can predict the answer to a maths question. • I can count backwards from a given number. • I can listen to other children and ask questions.

Supporting resources

Find out more about centipedes at:
• http://www.bbc.co.uk/nature/wildfacts/factfiles/414.shtml

Challenge Plan: Year 1

D1: names of common 2D shapes; features of familiar 2D shapes; counting back 1; subtracting a 1-digit number from a 'teens' number

Summary

Y1 ⭐ D1.5

Money banks

Pairs or groups working independently

Year 1 Challenge Workbook page 14

Money bank; collection of coins up to 10p

Abacus Evolve objectives

- Subtract one 1-digit number from another

Framework objectives

- Understand subtraction as 'take away' and find a 'difference' by counting up; use practical and informal written methods to support the subtraction of a 1-digit number from a 1-digit or 2-digit number and a multiple of 10 from a 2-digit number
- Solve problems involving counting, adding, subtracting, doubling or halving in the context of numbers, measures or money, for example to 'pay' and 'give change'
- Retell stories, ordering events using story language

Teacher notes

Getting started
Explain to children that they are going to work together to solve a problem about money. The problem is about a money bank – make sure they know what this is. If possible have one available for the children to explore.

Activity
Children work from Workbook page 14. They see pictures of three money banks with coins visible inside. They draw lines to match the money banks to three children, based on information about the amount of money each child has.
Once children have done this, they work in pairs to compare their answers.

Extra help
Provide 1p coins laid out in sets to match the amounts in the three money banks. This will allow children to take away 1p to find the answer. Focus on exchanging the pennies for other coins, for example 2p is 2 × 1p.

Further extension
Each child is given 10p pocket money each week. How much money will each child have in their money bank next week? How many weeks will it take to save up 50p?

If you have time
Encourage children to talk about why they have linked the money banks in the way that they have. Do they want to change their mind having listened to their partner? Explain to children that it is okay to change your mind. Discuss with children how they might show this in their book. Encourage them not to rub out or scribble over the answer.
Would you rather have 1p pocket money each day, or 10p each week?

Be aware

- Relating problem solving in books to a context, requires children to understand the ideas in the problem and apply them to a range of different scenarios. Using words and pictures to do this is an important skill.

Outcomes

- I can use clues to solve problems.
- I can tell a story to a partner which links to the problem.

Supporting resources

- Children can practise making choices and decisions by reading *Would you rather?* by John Burningham published by Red Fox (ISBN 978-0-099200-41-3).

D1: names of common 2D shapes; features of familiar 2D shapes; counting back 1; subtracting a 1-digit number from a 'teens' number

Summary

Y1 ⭐ D1.6

Skittles

Pairs or groups working independently

Year 1 Challenge PCM 18

20 small plastic bottles; sand; small ball; counters; dice

Abacus Evolve objectives

- **Y2** Extend understanding of subtraction as taking away

Framework objectives

- **Y2** Add or subtract mentally a 1-digit number or a multiple of 10 to or from any 2-digit number; use practical and informal written methods to add and subtract 2-digit numbers
- **Y2** Understand that subtraction is the inverse of addition and vice versa; use this to derive and record related addition and subtraction number sentences
- **Y2** Solve problems involving addition, subtraction, multiplication or division in contexts of numbers, measures or pounds and pence

Teacher notes

Preparation
Half fill 20 small plastic bottles (for example fizzy drinks bottles) with sand, so that they stand up.

Getting started
Stand the 20 bottles in rows, like skittles, on the floor. *You will play a skittles game, taking turns to roll a ball and knock down as many skittles as you can. If you knock down the last skittle, you're the winner.*

Activity
Children take turns rolling the ball to knock down skittles. Let the children identify issues, for example *it's not fair if one person rolls the balls from nearer to the skittles.* Encourage them to make up their rules for a 'fair' game. Children play the game removing any skittles that get knocked down. *Does it make a difference who wins if you go first? How could you make this fair?*

Children work from PCM 18. They play the same game, using dice and pictures. Children take it in turns to roll a dice and cross out the matching number of skittles. They continue taking turns until there are no skittles left and the winner is declared. Pairs play again and discuss who will go first and whether it makes a difference.

Pairs then play the game on the score card on PCM 18. They start with the number 20 and take away the number on the dice each time they throw it. The winner is the first to get to 0. Encourage careful scoring.

Extra help
Use 10 skittles instead of 20.

Further extension
Use different contexts and numbers. For example, *there are 30 marbles in a jar; throw two dice and remove that number of marbles from the jar.* Ask children to write a number sentence with the answer before checking.

Be aware

- Even when children know subtraction facts to 20, it is important that they can explain in words and pictures how they relate to real-life contexts.

Outcomes

- I can subtract numbers in a range of real-life contexts.

Supporting resources

Children can find more strategy games here:
- http://nrich.maths.org/public/viewer.php?obj_id=2761
- http://nrich.maths.org/public/viewer.php?obj_id=1189

Challenge Plan: Year 1

E1: doubling numbers up to 5; adding using near doubles; recognising and ordering coins; exchanging coins and finding totals

Summary

Y1 ⭐ E1.1

Granny's knitting

A small group working with an adult

Year 1 Challenge Workbook page 15

Knitting needles; wool; counters or cubes (optional)

Abacus Evolve objectives

- Recognise doubling as the addition of two equal amounts
- Know by heart doubles for numbers up to at least 5
- Begin to know by heart doubles for numbers up to at least 10

Framework objectives

- Recall the doubles of all numbers to at least 10
- Describe a puzzle or problem using numbers, practical materials and diagrams; use these to solve the problem and set the solution in the original context
- Ask and answer questions, make relevant contributions, offer suggestions

Teacher notes

Preparation

Ask members of staff or parents if they have some knitting needles and wool you can borrow. Collect several examples of knitting, still on needles.

Activity

- Show children some knitting and point out the stitches on the needles.
- Look at Workbook page 15 together. Tell children the story of Granny's knitting: *She begins with two stitches on her needles. On the second row she doubles the number of stitches. How many stitches does she have on her needles when she knits the second row?* (4) *How do you know? Granny continues like this, doubling the number of stitches on each row.*
- Children work from Workbook page 15. They fill in the table to show the number of stitches in rows 1 to 5.
- Bring the group back together to compare answers. *How did you work these out? Can you see any patterns in the numbers?* Discuss children's responses.
- Look together at the second picture on the Workbook page, and work through the final three questions together. You may need to explain the concept of 'dropped' stitches, and show what you mean by deliberately dropping stitches on some real knitting.

Extra help

Children could use counters or cubes to model the number of stitches, pairing up items and counting in 2s.

Alternatively, they could use drawings, such as a sketch of a needle with stitches on it.

Further extension

Ask children to explore what happens if Granny starts with three stitches on the first row instead of two.

The investigation could be extended to cover other starting numbers.

If you have time

Granny needs new glasses. She is seeing double! She is busy doing some knitting and every time she knits two stitches she thinks she has done four. She looks at her knitting needles and counts eight stitches. How many stitches has she really got on her needles?

Be aware

- Children may need support to understand how knitting works. If someone in the school knits it makes the context more realistic. Children may not realise that stitches transfer from one needle to the other.

Outcomes

- I can double small numbers.
- I can describe how I used doubles to solve a problem.

Supporting resources

Children can practise doubling with this game:
- http://www.bbc.co.uk/schools/numbertime/games/dartboard.shtml

E1: doubling numbers up to 5; adding using near doubles; recognising and ordering coins; exchanging coins and finding totals

Summary

Y1 ☆ E1.2   **Double-buttoned coat**

Individuals or pairs working independently

Year 1 Challenge Workbook page 16

Buttons or counters (optional); cut-outs of double-breasted coats (optional)

Abacus Evolve objectives

- Recognise doubling as the addition of two equal amounts
- Know by heart doubles for numbers up to at least 5
- Begin to know by heart doubles for numbers up to at least 10

Framework objectives

- Recall the doubles of all numbers to at least 10
- Solve problems involving counting, adding, subtracting, doubling or halving in the context of numbers, measures or money, for example to 'pay' and 'give change'

Teacher notes

Preparation
You may want to collect some buttons or counters and make a few cut-outs of double-breasted coats.

Alternatively, you could photocopy and enlarge the pictures on Workbook page 16.

Getting started
Look at Workbook page 16 together. *Finn is a fashion designer. He has designed a coat which is double-buttoned – it has buttons on both sides. The number of buttons on the right-hand side must match the number of buttons on the left-hand side.*

Activity
Children work from Workbook page 16. They complete a picture of a double-buttoned coat, so that the two sides match. They then draw numbers of buttons of their choice on three coats, making sure the buttons on both sides match. They write the total number of buttons on each coat.
Children work how many buttons will be on each side if Finn sews on 24 buttons altogether. They then think about how many buttons there would be in total if Finn sewed the same number of buttons on the back.

Extra help
Use smaller numbers and give each child a cut-out of a coat to place buttons/counters on.

Further extension
The army have ordered 12 new coats as part of their uniform. Each coat has six buttons down each side. When the coats arrive the buttons are missing. How many new buttons need to be ordered and stitched in place?

If you have time
Ask children to design coats with three rows of buttons instead of two. *How would you arrange 12 buttons into three rows?*

Information
In the Extra activity on the Workbook page there are seven possible answers:

2 coats with 24 buttons	3 coats with 16 buttons
4 coats with 12 buttons	6 coats with 8 buttons
8 coats with 6 buttons	12 coats with 4 buttons
24 coats with 2 buttons.	

Children do not need to find all seven answers, but should be encouraged to find at least two or three of them.

Be aware

- Children may not realise that doubling is the same as multiplying by 2 so developing these links is important.

Outcomes

- I can find doubles by organising two equal groups of buttons.

Challenge Plan: Year 1

E1: doubling numbers up to 5; adding using near doubles; recognising and ordering coins; exchanging coins and finding totals

Summary

Y1 ⭐ E1.3

Next door numbers

Pairs working independently

Year 1 Challenge PCM 19

Abacus Evolve objectives

- Add by identifying near doubles for numbers up to 10
- Recognise doubling as the addition of two equal amounts
- Begin to know by heart doubles for numbers up to at least 10

Framework objectives

- Recall the doubles of all numbers to at least 10
- Describe a puzzle or problem using numbers, practical materials and diagrams; use these to solve the problem and set the solution in the original context

Teacher notes

Preparation
Photocopy PCM 19, one copy per pair.

Getting started
Give each pair a copy of PCM 19. Read through the game description together, ensuring children understand the instructions.

Activity
Children play the next door number game in pairs. They take turns to choose a pair of doors next to each other, and add the numbers using doubles. For example, if they choose doors 4 and 5, they would work out 4 + 5 mentally by doubling 4 and adding 1. They score points to match the answer, for example for 4 + 5 = 9, they would score 9 points. Children should check each other's answers before awarding points. When a child has used two door numbers, they cross them out so they can't be used again. Children play until all the doors are crossed out or until no more pairs of doors can be chosen. The winner is the child with the higher total score.

Extra help
Draw eight doors on a separate sheet of paper, and write the numbers 1–8 on them. Ask children to play the game as described on the PCM.

Further extension
Draw 10 doors on a separate sheet of paper, and write the numbers 14–23 on them. Ask children to play the game as described on the PCM.

If you have time
Can you add three next door numbers together? Challenge children to find a quick way of working out the total.

Information
A quick way of finding the total of three consecutive numbers is to multiply the middle number by 3. In the context of this lesson this could be explained as doubling the middle number and then adding the middle number on again. For example, the total of 9 + 10 + 11 is 30, which is 3 times the middle number, or double the middle number (double 10 = 20) and then add the middle number on again (20 + 10 = 30).

Be aware

- The purpose of the activity is to look for near doubles to support addition of two numbers. Supporting children in using strategies that are more efficient than counting in 1s is an important part of this lesson.

Outcomes

- I can use near doubles to add two 'next door' numbers together.

Supporting resources

Investigate placing + and – signs between four consecutive numbers to give different totals:
- http://nrich.maths.org/public/viewer.php?obj_id=31

Challenge Plan: Year 1

E1: doubling numbers up to 5; adding using near doubles; recognising and ordering coins; exchanging coins and finding totals

Summary

Y1 ⭐ E1.4

Paying for parking

Pairs working independently

Year 1 Challenge PCM 20

Real or plastic 1p, 2p, 5p and 10p coins; 20p coins (optional); photographs of parking machines (optional)

Abacus Evolve objectives

- **Y2** Read the time to the hour and half hour on analogue and 12-hour digital clocks
- **Y2** Recognise all coins and begin to use £·p notation for money
- **Y2** Find totals of sets of coins; relate to adding three or more numbers
- **Y2** Pay an exact sum using smaller coins up to £2

Framework objectives

- **Y2** *Use units of time (seconds, minutes, hours, days) and know the relationships between them; read the time to the quarter hour; identify time intervals, including those that cross the hour*
- **Y2** *Solve problems involving addition, subtraction, multiplication or division in contexts of numbers, measures or pounds and pence*
- **Y2** *Explain their views to others in a small group; decide how to report the group's views to the class*

Teacher notes

Preparation
Photocopy PCM 20, one copy per pair.

Getting started
Look at PCM 20 and discuss paying for parking tickets at a machine. Point out the notice with the charges on it and the digital display on the machine, showing the time. Make sure children understand that this means it is 12 noon. Give children 1p, 2p, 5p and 10p coins for them to look at. Some children may like to use the coins when working out their answers.

Activity
Children work from PCM 20. They investigate different ways of paying for a ticket using the coins available, and record these carefully. Children are also asked to work out when Mr Biggs must get back to his car. The current time is shown as a digital display on the machine. If you have an opportunity, encourage children to share their methods as a group and discuss how systematic they were.

Extra help
Use 1p and 2p coins only.

Further extension
Increase the parking charges to 25p for 1 hour and 40p for 2 hours. Include 20p coins in the change as well.

If you have time
Bring in photographs of a range of parking machines so that children can practise reading the various times and amounts charged. You could discuss which machines offer the cheapest and most expensive parking.

Be aware

- To find the possible coin combinations children need to be systematic in their thinking and recording. This is challenging for young children. It may be helpful to have plenty of coins so that children record the various combinations by laying out rows of coins and ordering them.

Outcomes

- I can find out how many different ways there are to pay for a parking ticket.
- I can read the time on a digital clock.

Supporting resources

Try the Five Coins problem:
- http://nrich.maths.org/public/viewer.php?obj_id=142

E1: doubling numbers up to 5; adding using near doubles; recognising and ordering coins; exchanging coins and finding totals

Summary

Y1 ⭐ E1.5

What did she buy?

Pairs working independently

Year 1 Challenge Workbook page 17

50p, 20p, 10p, 5p, 2p and 1p coins (real or plastic); supermarket till receipts (optional)

Abacus Evolve objectives

- Begin to recognise that more than two numbers can be added together
- Add a 1-digit number to a 2-digit number, crossing a multiple of 10
- Recognise coins of different values
- Find totals of sets of coins
- Pay an exact sum using smaller coins up to 50p

Framework objectives

- Relate addition to counting on; recognise that addition can be done in any order, use practical and informal written methods to support the addition of a 1-digit number or a multiple of 10 to a 1-digit or 2-digit number
- Solve problems involving counting, adding, subtracting, doubling or halving in the context of numbers, measures or money, for example to 'pay' and 'give change'
- Describe ways of solving puzzles and problems, explaining choices and decisions orally or using pictures
- Explain their views to others in a small group, and decide how to report the group's views to the class

Teacher notes

Getting started
Make sure children understand what to do on the Workbook page. Leave some coins out on the table for them to look at and use in their investigation.

Activity
Children work from Workbook page 17. They look at a picture of items in a shop arranged on six shelves. The items on each shelf are worth a different amount. Children are told that Mrs Button spent 50p. They work out which items she could have bought for that amount. Children then compare answers and discuss what they notice. They are then challenged to come up with other ways that Mrs Button might have spent 50p. They should consider how many different possibilities there might be.

Extra help
Tell children that Mrs Button only spends 20p in the shop. This makes the calculations simpler, but doubles the number of possible coin combinations.

Further extension
All the prices have increased by 10p an item. How much more money will Mrs Button need if she wants to buy the same items?

If you have time
Collect till receipts from a supermarket and discuss the way the lists are organised. *Is it easy to check how much you have spent?*

Information
There are 18 different ways Mrs Button could have spent 50p:
one 50p item = 3 ways;
two 25p items = 1 way;
one 25p item + two 10p items + one 5p item = 10 ways;
one 25p item + two 10p items + two 2p items + one 1p item = 2 ways;
one 25p item + five 5p items = 2 ways.

There are 36 different ways Mrs Button could have spent 20p:
two 10p items = 1 way;
four 5p items = 5 ways;
one 10p item + two 5p items = 20 ways;
three 5p items + two 2p items + one 1p item = 10 ways.

Be aware

- Children may have limited experience of shopping with money and they may need support to exchange different denominations.

Outcomes

- I can find totals of sets of coins.
- I can find different ways of spending the same amount of money.

Supporting resources

Children could try solving this problem involving different ways to put 10 coins into three puddings:
- http://nrich.maths.org/public/viewer.php?obj_id=1030

Challenge Plan: Year 1

E1: doubling numbers up to 5; adding using near doubles; recognising and ordering coins; exchanging coins and finding totals

---

Summary

Y1 ⬡ E1.6

Money changer

A small group working with an adult

Year 1 Challenge PCM 21

Photographs of change machines and change sorters (optional); 1p, 2p and 10p coins (optional)

Abacus Evolve objectives

- Recognise coins of different values
- Exchange coins for equivalent in 10p and 1p coins
- Find totals of sets of coins
- Pay an exact sum using smaller coins up to 50p
- Solve 'real-life' problems involving money (change)
- Begin to recognise that more than two numbers can be added together
- Add a 1-digit number to a 2-digit number, crossing a multiple of 10

Framework objectives

- Relate addition to counting on; recognise that addition can be done in any order, use practical and informal written methods to support the addition of a 1-digit number or a multiple of 10 to a 1-digit or 2-digit number
- Solve problems involving counting, adding, subtracting, doubling or halving in the context of numbers, measures or money, for example to 'pay' and 'give change'
- Describe a puzzle or problem using numbers, practical materials and diagrams; use these to solve the problem and set the solution in the original context
- Retell stories, ordering events using story language

Teacher notes

Preparation
Photocopy PCM 21, one copy per child.
If possible, collect some photographs of various types of change machines and change sorters.

Activity
- If possible, show photographs of money changing machines, explaining what they do and how they work.
- Talk about situations in which you might need to use a change machine in order to get certain types of coins, for example for machines selling train tickets or parking tickets; for washers and driers in a laundrette.
- Introduce the scenario on PCM 21. Ask children questions about using the money changing machine. For example: *You need one 10p coin. What coins could you put into the machine? Could you put a different set of coins in to get 10p?*
- Read through the questions together, ensuring children understand what they are being asked to do. Children work in pairs to answer the questions. They may want to use real or plastic coins or paper and pencil jottings to support them in their calculations.
- Finally, children work individually to make up their own word problems using the change machine idea. Talk with children about their ideas, and help them present their questions if necessary.

Extra help
Use 1p coins only to practise swapping for 10p. Ask children to make up stories to explain what they are doing.

Further extension
Use 1p, 2p and 5p coins to create other stories about Mr Jin and the change machine.

Be aware

- Some children may never have used a change machine and so the concept will need some explanation.

Outcomes

- I can swap coins for other coins worth the same amount.
- I can solve word problems involving money.

Challenge Plan: Year 1

A2: counting on and back in 1s, 10s or 100s; recognising odd and even numbers; understanding and using ordinal numbers; ordering numbers

Summary

Y1 A2.1

Number words

Individuals or pairs working independently

Year 1 Challenge Workbook page 18

1–100 square or 1–100 number line (optional); raffle tickets showing numbers over 100 (optional)

Abacus Evolve objectives

- Write numbers up to 10 in words and up to 11 in figures
- Begin to read numbers up to 100 in words and figures
- Begin to partition 2-digit numbers into T and U
- Recognise the value of each digit in a 'teens' number

Framework objectives

- *Read and write numerals from 0 to 20, then beyond; use knowledge of place value to position these numbers on a number track and number line*
- *Describe simple patterns and relationships involving numbers or shapes; decide whether examples satisfy given conditions*

Teacher notes

Getting started
Look at Workbook page 18. Read the number words as a group. Talk through how to combine one of the unit words with one of the decade words to write a 2-digit number in words. Ask children to write a few 2-digit numbers in words, including a 'teens' number. Explain what children must do on the Workbook page.

Activity
Children work from Workbook page 18. They complete the grid. Children then write the number words to match the figures shown, using the word cards on the page to help them. They then colour each number on the grid.

Extra help
A complete 1–100 square or a 1–100 number line would provide useful support.

Further extension
Challenge each child to write their door number in words, or give them a raffle ticket showing a number greater than 100 and ask them to write that number in words.

Be aware

- Children often find combining words like this quite difficult. Model using word cards (e.g. names of units and decade numbers) if necessary.

Outcomes

- I can write numbers to 99 in words.

Supporting resources

Number words *one* to *nine* and decade words *twenty* to *one hundred*, written on blank cards, could be useful.

Challenge Plan: Year 1

A2: counting on and back in 1s, 10s or 100s; recognising odd and even numbers; understanding and using ordinal numbers; ordering numbers

Summary

Y1 A2.2

Counting in 10s

Individuals working independently

Year 1 Challenge Workbook page 19

Colouring pencils in nine different colours; 10 by 10 blank grids (optional); 1–100 square (optional)

Abacus Evolve objectives

- Begin to read numbers up to 100 in words and figures
- Count on and back in 10s from a 1-digit number

Framework objectives

- *Read and write numerals from 0 to 20, then beyond; use knowledge of place value to position these numbers on a number track and number line*
- *Derive and recall all pairs of numbers with a total of 10 and addition facts for totals to at least 5; work out the corresponding subtraction facts*
- *Describe simple patterns and relationships involving numbers or shapes; decide whether examples satisfy given conditions*

Teacher notes

Preparation
Cut some 10 by 10 grids from squared paper for the 'Further extension' activity.

Getting started
Look at Workbook page 19. Discuss the three shaded numbers: 5, 15, 25. *Can anyone tell me the rule for this sequence? What would the next number be? You are going to shade the rest of the numbers in the sequence. Each number is next to the one before, and you can move horizontally, vertically or diagonally.* Explain that once children have completed this sequence, they will find and colour the other eight sequences in the grid, filling in the missing numbers as they go.

Activity
Children work from Workbook page 19. They shade the rest of the sequence that starts with 5 and counts on in 10s. They then find and shade the other eight sequences, which each start from a 1-digit number and count on in 10s. When a path crosses a blank square, they fill in the missing number.

Extra help
You could write out a couple of the sequences for children, to give them a starting point.

Alternatively, a 1–100 square would provide useful support.

Further extension
Give children blank 10 by 10 grids and ask them to create their own paths counting on in 10s. They can then swap with their partner and colour each other's paths.

Information
These are the missing numbers:

34	31	87
14	41	50
51	4	47

Be aware

- Depending on the order in which children complete the paths, they may need to make some corrections to the missing numbers. Have some sticky labels ready to cover up errors if the children have chosen a dark colour for that particular path.

Outcomes

- I can count on in 10s from any 1-digit number.

Challenge Plan: Year 1

A2: counting on and back in 1s, 10s or 100s; recognising odd and even numbers; understanding and using ordinal numbers; ordering numbers

Summary

Y1 ⭐ **A2.3**	**10 more, 10 less**	
	Individuals working independently	
	Year 1 Challenge Workbook page 20	
	1–100 square (optional)	

Abacus Evolve objectives

- **Y2** Count on and back in 1s or 10s from a 2- or 3-digit number
- **Y2** Begin to read and write numbers up to 1000 in figures
- **Y2** Begin to partition 3-digit numbers into H, T and U

Framework objectives

- **Y2** Read and write 2- and 3-digit numbers in figures and words; describe and extend number sequences and recognise odd and even numbers
- **Y2** *Count up to 100 objects by grouping them and counting in 10s, 5s or 2s; explain what each digit in a 2-digit number represents, including numbers where 0 is a place holder; partition 2-digit numbers in different ways, including into multiples of 10 and 1*
- **Y2** Describe patterns and relationships involving numbers or shapes, make predictions and test these with examples

Teacher notes

Getting started
Look at Workbook page 20. *Which number comes after 46 if you are counting on in 10s? So what number comes after 146? Which number comes before 146 if you are counting back in 10s?* Focus on the fact that the units and hundreds digits do not change; only the tens digit increases or decreases by one ten.

Activity
Children work from Workbook page 20. They complete the sets of three numbers, counting on or back in 10s as appropriate.

Extra help
A 1–100 square would provide useful support.

If you have time
Write a large number on a piece of paper, such as *6 234 587*. Read it to children and ask them to talk to each other and try to count on (or back) in 10s from this number. They should write the numbers, not try to say them! Ask children to write other large numbers and challenge a partner to count on or back in 10s.

Information
Accept arrangements which count back, such as 62, 52, 42, as well as 42, 52, 62, since the order has not been specified. Those who are more proficient with numbers may well choose to reverse the usual direction of counting as they explore numbers.

Be aware

- Children easily lapse into counting on or back in 1s. If this happens, ask them to read their numbers aloud and they will usually notice what they have done.

Outcomes

- I can find the number which is 10 more or 10 less than any 2- or 3-digit number.

Challenge Plan: Year 1

A2: counting on and back in 1s, 10s or 100s; recognising odd and even numbers; understanding and using ordinal numbers; ordering numbers

Summary

Y1 A2.4

Colouring to order

Pairs working independently

Year 1 Challenge Workbook page 21

Year 1 Challenge PCM 22

Thin card; bags; colour-spot dice; colouring pencils to match the spots on the dice; sticky labels (optional); 1–20 number track (optional)

Abacus Evolve objectives

- Understand and use ordinal numbers up to at least 20th

Framework objectives

- Compare and order numbers, using the related vocabulary; use the equals (=) sign
- Ask and answer questions, make relevant contributions, offer suggestions and take turns

Teacher notes

Preparation
Photocopy PCM 22 on to thin card, one copy per pair. Cut out the cards and put each set in a bag.

You will need one colour-spot dice for each pair. If you do not have any, make some by covering each side of a normal dice with a sticker. Draw a different colour spot on each face.

Getting started
Look at the scarf on Workbook page 21. Show children the order cards from PCM 22. Put them in a bag. Demonstrate taking one card from the bag at random, and rolling a colour-spot dice. *The card tells you which stripe to colour on your scarf, and the dice tells you which colour to use. You will take turns to take a card and roll the dice, then colour a stripe on your scarf to match. After your turn, put the card back in the bag. If the stripe is already coloured, you miss a turn. Keep playing until the scarf is completely coloured. The winner is the first person to complete their scarf.*

Activity
Children work from Workbook page 21. They play the game in pairs, each colouring their own scarf on the Workbook page.

Extra help
If children find it hard to work out which stripe is which, suggest that they number the stripes.

Alternatively, you could give them a 1–20 number track.

If the game is taking too long, ask children to put each card to one side (rather than returning it to the bag) once both players have coloured the corresponding stripe.

Be aware

- The ordinal cards show both the number and the word to help prevent confusion.

Outcomes

- I can use ordinal numbers up to 20th.

Challenge Plan: Year 1

Summary

Y1 A2.5

Beads

A small group working with an adult

Year 1 Challenge Workbook page 22

Red, yellow and blue colouring pencils; a set of threading beads (optional)

Abacus Evolve objectives	Framework objectives
• Understand and use ordinal numbers up to at least 20th	• Compare and order numbers, using the related vocabulary; use the equals (=) sign • Describe a puzzle or problem using numbers, practical materials and diagrams; use these to solve the problem and set the solution in the original context • Describe ways of solving puzzles and problems, explaining choices and decisions orally or using pictures • Take turns to speak, listen to others' suggestions and talk about what they are going to do

Teacher notes

Activity

• Show children Workbook page 22. Talk through the repeating pattern of the beads. *What is the pattern? What colour will the next bead be? How do you know?*
• Children work from Workbook page 22. They colour the beads the appropriate colours to show the answers.
• Some children will find it helpful to continue the bead string by drawing dots of colour or by using the initial letter of the colours: *r y b r y b* … Others will be able to say the pattern as they count along to the appropriate position.
• Ask children to explain how they worked out the answers. If a variety of methods have been used within the group, encourage discussion about which methods worked well.
• *Can anyone work out what colour the 30th bead would be?* (blue) *How did you work it out?*

Extra help

If a child is struggling to identify the colour of a bead they cannot actually see, they could make the bead string shown and continue the pattern so that all the questions can be answered by counting along the beads. Alternatively, they might like to draw the beads.

Be aware	Outcomes
• For children who reach the Extra activity, make sure they confirm which end their pattern starts from before asking each other questions. It is very easy to focus on the wrong end when children are facing each other.	• I can use ordinal numbers up to 20th. • I can answer questions about order. • I can continue a sequence of colours, and work out the next colour.

Supporting resources

A 1–20 number line or track might be useful, as children could mark the colours below the appropriate numbers.

Challenge Plan: Year 1

A2: counting on and back in 1s, 10s or 100s; recognising odd and even numbers; understanding and using ordinal numbers; ordering numbers

Summary

Y1 ⬡ A2.6

Between

A small group working with an adult

Year 1 Challenge Workbook page 23

Red, blue, green, purple, orange and yellow colouring pencils; counters (optional); 0–10 number line marked in $\frac{1}{2}$s (optional)

Abacus Evolve objectives

- Begin to say a number lying between two numbers
- Say a number lying between two numbers up to at least 50

Framework objectives

- Compare and order numbers, using the related vocabulary; use the equals (=) sign
- Listen to and follow instructions accurately, asking for help and clarification if necessary

Teacher notes

Activity
- Look at the Workbook page. Make sure children understand what is meant by 'the numbers between'.
- Children work from Workbook page 23. They colour the numbers that lie between two specified numbers.
- Make sure children are not colouring the numbers mentioned. If children need a mental image to help them to remember this, you could describe the specified numbers as the fences holding the other numbers in between them.
- Ask children to compare their grid with a partner. *Do your grids look the same?* If there are any discrepancies, encourage discussion and explanation of children's methods.

Extra help
Ask children to put a counter on each of the specified numbers. This should help them to see which numbers are between them, and stop them from colouring the specified numbers.

Further extension
Ask children to take turns to ask the group a question, such as: *'Can you tell me one number that is between 24 and 36?'* The rest of the group have to agree an answer before giving it.

Ask children to find the number half-way between 6 and 9. Give them a number line marked in $\frac{1}{2}$s to help them.

Information
Although children will be familiar with 'half' and even 'half-way between', they may well see half and half-way as vague terms. You will probably need to show the children how to locate the two end points (you could use the image of fences, as described above) and move towards the middle equally from both ends.

Be aware

- Some children find 'between' a difficult concept and will continue to include one or more end points. Demonstrate with concrete objects.

Outcomes

- I can find the numbers between two given numbers.

Challenge Plan: Year 1

B2: addition and subtraction facts for pairs that total up to 10; adding three 1-digit numbers; right angles; clockwise and anticlockwise turns

Summary

Y1 ⭐ B2.1   **It's in the balance**

A small group working with an adult

A number balance (equaliser) and weights

◁∞▷   Abacus Evolve objectives
• Know by heart addition facts for pairs of numbers that total up to 7 • Begin to use the + and = signs to record addition sentences • Begin to recognise that addition can be done in any order • Begin to recognise that more than two numbers can be added together • Know by heart addition and subtraction facts for pairs of numbers that total 10

Framework objectives
• *Derive and recall all pairs of numbers with a total of 10 and addition facts for totals to at least 5; work out the corresponding subtraction facts* • *Use the vocabulary related to addition and subtraction and symbols to describe and record addition and subtraction number sentences* • *Relate addition to counting on; recognise that addition can be done in any order; use practical and informal written methods to support the addition of a 1-digit number or a multiple of 10 to a 1-digit or 2-digit number*

Teacher notes

Preparation
If you don't have a number balance, you could use an online version (see 'Supporting resources' below).

Activity

• Show the number balance. *This is called an equaliser. We can hang weights below the numbers. To make the two sides balance, they must each have the same value.*
• Give children time to play with the equaliser.
• Explain to children that = means equals. *In order for things to be equal there must be the same value either side of the equals sign.*
• Hang a weight from number 2 on the right-hand side of the equaliser. *What would you need to do to make the equaliser balanced again? How will you know if it's balanced? What will happen?* Invite one or two children to hang a weight on the left-hand side to see if they can make it balance.
• Next hang a weight from number 7 on the right-hand side of the equaliser. Ask children to work in pairs. *How many different ways are there of balancing the equaliser? What could you do? Record your answers, then test them on the equaliser.*
• Challenge the class to use as many or as few weights as they want to give both sides of the equaliser a value of 10. *How many different ways are there?* Make sure they record their answers using + and = symbols.

Extra help
Ask children to always use three weights – two on the left-hand side and one on the right – to make simple additions such as 2 + 5 = 7.

Further extension
Imagine that you have a 'weight' that is zero. How do you think this would change the equaliser? Try adding some zeros to your number sentences. What happens? Discuss with a partner.

Be aware

• Children may be confused because we use 'weight' in everyday language when we actually mean 'mass'. Refer to your school policy on this issue as it relates to other areas of the curriculum such as science and a consistent approach is helpful.

Outcomes

• I know pairs of numbers that total up to 10.

Supporting resources

Use this online number balance:
• http://nrich.maths.org/public/viewer.php?obj_id=4725

Challenge Plan: Year 1

B2: addition and subtraction facts for pairs that total up to 10; adding three 1-digit numbers; right angles; clockwise and anticlockwise turns

Summary

Y1 ☆ B2.2

Hidden numbers

Pairs working independently

Year 1 Challenge PCMs 23 and 24

Counters in two colours; digit cards (optional); + and = cards (optional); 1–10 number tracks (optional); 6-sided dice (optional); counters (optional)

Abacus Evolve objectives

- Know by heart addition and subtraction facts for pairs of numbers that total up to 8
- Relate number bonds to an understanding of addition, including use of +, −, =

Framework objectives

- *Derive and recall all pairs of numbers with a total of 10 and addition facts for totals to at least 5; work out the corresponding subtraction facts*
- *Use the vocabulary related to addition and subtraction and symbols to describe and record addition and subtraction number sentences*
- *Listen to and follow instructions accurately, asking for help and clarification if necessary*

Teacher notes

Preparation
Photocopy PCMs 23 and 24, one copy of each per pair. Cut up the additions on PCM 23.

Provide counters, one each per child. Make sure each pair has two different-coloured counters.

Getting started
Give pairs the cut-out additions from PCM 23. Explain the game to them: one person in the pair chooses an addition without showing it to the other person. They cover one digit using a square of card, then reveal the missing-number addition. The other person has to work out the missing number and record the complete addition. The first person removes the card to check whether they are right. They take turns to do this.

Give pairs PCM 24. Explain that they will use the blank additions to test out how many numbers they have to fill in so that their partner can work out the missing numbers. If they run out of blank additions, they can use digit cards and + and = cards to form the additions.

Activity
In pairs, children take turns to hide a digit in one of the additions from PCM 23. Their partner works out the missing number and records the addition. They check by revealing the missing number.

Pairs then use the blank additions on PCM 24 to investigate how many numbers they must fill in so that their partner can work out the missing number(s).

Extra help
Give pairs digit cards 0–5 and + and = cards. Ask them to use the cards to make simple additions.

Further extension
Challenge children to create their own version of the game, using the blank additions on PCM 24 and filling them in with larger numbers.

If you have time
Ask children to create their own game involving missing-number additions and a 1–10 number track. Each time a player works out the missing number, they roll a dice and move their counter forward one space on the number track. The winner is the first to reach 10.

Be aware

- The idea that an equation must balance is important as it forms the basis for mathematical expressions. Some children may use the = sign to indicate the next step in an answer instead of to indicate that both sides are equal.

Outcomes

- I know pairs of numbers that total 8.
- I can work out the missing number in an addition.

B2: addition and subtraction facts for pairs that total up to 10; adding three 1-digit numbers; right angles; clockwise and anticlockwise turns

Summary

Y1 ☆ **B2.3**

Shortcuts

Pairs working independently

Year 1 Challenge PCM 25

Small whiteboard (optional)

Abacus Evolve objectives

- Know by heart addition and subtraction facts for pairs of numbers that total up to 9
- Record addition and subtraction facts for pairs of numbers that total up to 9, using +, − and = in number sentences
- Begin to use patterns of similar calculations (e.g. 10 − 0 = 10, 10 − 1 = 9, 10 − 2 = 8, …)

Framework objectives

- *Derive and recall all pairs of numbers with a total of 10 and addition facts for totals to at least 5; work out the corresponding subtraction facts*
- *Use the vocabulary related to addition and subtraction and symbols to describe and record addition and subtraction number sentences*
- *Describe simple patterns and relationships involving numbers or shapes; decide whether examples satisfy given conditions*
- *Explain their views to others in a small group, and decide how to report the group's views to the class*

Teacher notes

Preparation
Photocopy PCM 25, one copy per pair.

Getting started
Give children PCM 25. *Rafael has finished all 10 calculations but everyone else in the class is still on the first one! How do you think he did them so quickly? Work with a partner to try to find his shortcut. Then you're going to make up some calculations like this, and swap with another pair to see if they can find your shortcut.*

Activity
Children work from PCM 25. They discuss how Rafael might have solved the equations quickly. (He spotted the pattern, so he knew that each answer would be 1 less than the previous answer.) They then make up their own series of questions that can be solved quickly using a shortcut. They swap sheets with another pair and try to answer the questions using a shortcut. Pairs then write a brief explanation of their shortcut.

Extra help
Create a simpler version of PCM 25, with a series of simple calculations such as this:
0 + 9 =
1 + 9 =
2 + 9 =

Further extension
Ask children to create word problems from their number sentences. For example, 2 + 8 − 1 = 10 − 1 could be: *The shop keeper was checking to see if he had the correct amount of money in the till. In the morning he had £2 in the till then he sold something for £8 – this was given to him as eight £1 coins. He added up what he had in the till. Then, he had to buy some stamps for £1. How much money did he have left?*

If you have time
Set up a classroom in the play corner, with a small whiteboard. Ask pairs to write calculations on the board and to get other children to write down their answers, explaining their methods.

Be aware

- Some children find it difficult to spot similar questions in calculations. If they cannot spot the shortcut they can complete the calculations in their own way; however, it may be helpful to pair them with someone else who is likely to spot the pattern and be able to explain it.

Outcomes

- I understand +, − and = in a number sentence.
- I can spot a pattern in similar calculations and use it to find the answers.

Challenge Plan: Year 1

B2: addition and subtraction facts for pairs that total up to 10; adding three 1-digit numbers; right angles; clockwise and anticlockwise turns

Summary

Y1 ☆ **B2.4**

What's my number?

Pairs working independently

Year 1 Challenge Workbook page 24

Year 1 Challenge PCM 26

Blank 3 by 3 grids, large enough for a playing card to fit in each cell (optional); two decks of playing cards (optional)

Abacus Evolve objectives	Framework objectives
• Describe position: above, below, beside, left, right	• Visualise and use everyday language to describe the position of objects and direction and distance when moving them, for example when placing or moving objects on a games board • Take turns to speak, listen to others' suggestions and talk about what they are going to do

Teacher notes

Preparation
Photocopy PCM 26, one copy per pair. Cut out the number cards.

Getting started
Look at Workbook page 24. Explain to children that they will be working in pairs to play a game where they have to guess the number their partner has chosen. Explain the rules, and give each pair a set of number cards.

Activity
Children work from Workbook page 24. They shuffle the cards and place them face down in a pile. One child chooses a card at random, without showing their partner. The card matches a number on the grid on the Workbook page. They describe the position of their card on the grid, using words such as *above*, *below*, *beside*, *left* and *right*. They must not say the number itself, but they can say other numbers on the grid. When their partner has guessed their number, they put the number card to one side, and it is their partner's turn. Pairs continue playing until they have used all the cards.

Extra help
Create a 3 by 3 grid and use numbers 10, 20, 30, 40, 50, 60, 70, 80, 90 or choose numbers relevant for the group.

Further extension
Children repeat the activity, but this time they must give three clues for each number. If their partner guesses it correctly after the first clue, the partner gets 3 points. If they guess it after the second clue they get 2 points. If they guess it after the third clue they get 1 point. They swap.

If you have time
Give children a blank 3 by 3 grid with cells large enough to fit a playing card in. Give them two sets of nine identical playing cards. Ask them to arrange one set of cards in the grid. They shuffle the other set and place them in a pile face down. They then play the game as on the Workbook page, taking turns to pick a card and describe its position on the grid relative to other cards. Make sure children are familiar with the names of the suits.

Be aware	Outcomes
• Positional language can be difficult for some children. Vocabulary cards can help with rehearsing the appropriate words.	• I can describe the position of something on a grid.

Supporting resources

This game of Incey Wincey Spider allows children to practise using the words *up* and *down*:
• http://nrich.maths.org/public/viewer.php?obj_id=5896

Challenge Plan: Year 1

B2: addition and subtraction facts for pairs that total up to 10; adding three 1-digit numbers; right angles; clockwise and anticlockwise turns

Summary

Y1 ⬠ B2.5

Turning around

A small group working with an adult

Year 1 Challenge Workbook page 25

Year 1 Challenge PCM 27

Geared clock; children's scissors; hard-backed book; egg box; spinner; padlock and key or wind-up toy; animal picture books (optional)

Abacus Evolve objectives

- Talk about things that turn
- Make whole turns, half turns and quarter turns

Framework objectives

- Identify objects that turn about a point (e.g. scissors) or about a line (e.g. a door); recognise and make whole, half and quarter turns
- Experiment with and build new stores of words to communicate in different contexts

Teacher notes

Preparation
Photocopy PCM 27, one copy per pair

Activity
- Explain to children that they are going to explore turning. Show all the objects you have collected that turn. Look at each object and discuss which parts of it turn and in what way.
- *Do all the objects turn one complete turn? Can some of them turn more than once? Do some of them only turn a small amount?* Encourage children to discuss these questions in pairs.
- Give each pair a copy of PCM 27. Ask them to sort the objects into those that turn a whole turn (or more) and those that do not. They write the names of the objects or draw pictures to record their decisions.
- Ask children to repeat for objects that turn a half turn, and those that turn less than a half turn.
- *Now think about you. Can you turn a whole turn? Less than a whole turn?* Ask children to stand up and try.
- *Now think about different body parts. What parts of your body can turn?*
- Children work from Workbook page 25.

Extra help
Start by focusing on the geared clock. Ask them to turn one of the hands given amounts, for example: *Make a turn that is less than a whole turn; Make a turn that is exactly a half turn.*

Further extension
Ask children to play 'follow my leader' in pairs. Child A walks a path with two turns in it. Child B watches, then follows the path as closely as possible. *Imagine Child A has ink on their feet – follow the ink!* Now Child A and B together draw the path on a piece of paper, showing the start and the finish and marking the turns. Children swap roles.

If you have time
Look at some animal books – which animals can turn quickly? Look at a picture of a crocodile. *What do you notice about its mouth? Can it turn its mouth? Can you make an egg box look like a crocodile's mouth?*

Be aware

- Objects can turn about a pivotal point or a line. Children may have troubling seeing both types. Understanding about turns helps children to recognise angles as measures of the amount of turn, for example a square corner is a quarter turn.

Outcomes

- I can use everyday language to describe turns.

Challenge Plan: Year 1

B2: addition and subtraction facts for pairs that total up to 10; adding three 1-digit numbers; right angles; clockwise and anticlockwise turns

Summary

Y1 ☆ B2.6

Obstacle course

Pairs working independently

Year 1 Challenge Workbook page 26

Year 1 Challenge PCM 28 (optional)

Coloured pencils; small items to use as obstacles (optional); floor robot (optional)

Abacus Evolve objectives

- Describe direction and movement: forwards, backwards, up, down, left, right
- Make whole turns, half turns and quarter turns

Framework objectives

- Visualise and use everyday language to describe the position of objects and direction and distance when moving them, for example when placing or moving objects on a game board
- Identify objects that turn about a point (e.g. scissors) or about a line (e.g. a door); recognise and make whole, half and quarter turns
- Describe ways of solving puzzles and problems, explaining choices and decisions orally or using pictures
- Listen with sustained concentration

Teacher notes

Preparation
Photocopy PCM 28 if you are planning to do the 'Further extension' activity.

Getting started
Look at the Workbook page. Explain what to do, and what vocabulary children should use.

Activity
Children work from Workbook page 26. They try to find the shortest route through the obstacle course, making sure they visit each obstacle. They can only move along the lines, and each move from one black dot to another counts as one step. Children mark their route on their grid using a coloured pencil. They then conceal their page from a partner and describe the route to them, using words such as *forwards*, *backwards*, *up*, *down*, *left*, *right*, *quarter turn*. They mark their partner's route on their grid using a different colour. They compare their routes.

Extra help
Make word cards such as *forwards*, *backwards*, *up*, *down*, *left* and *right* and leave these on the table for children to refer to.

Further extension
Give children a copy of PCM 28 each. One child places five small objects on the grid to represent obstacles, without their partner seeing. They describe where they have placed them to their partner, who tries to draw them in the same places. Children swap roles.

If you have time
Use a floor robot and programme a route for it to go to three different obstacles placed on the floor. Children work in pairs and give instructions to each other.

Be aware

- This lesson focuses on describing position using precise language. However, some children may decide to number the grid in some way. This is a precursor for developing work on coordinates, so should not necessarily be discouraged.

Outcomes

- I can find the shortest route around a grid.
- I can describe a route around a grid to a partner.

Challenge Plan: Year 1

C2: comparing weights; measuring weights; reading the time to the hour; organising and interpreting information in tables

Summary

Y1 C2.1

How heavy is a ball?

Pairs or groups working independently

Year 1 Challenge PCMs 29 and 30

A balance; a selection of balls in a range of sizes; felt pens; cubes; pegs; coins

Abacus Evolve objectives

- Compare two or more weights by direct comparison
- Estimate then measure weights, recording estimates
- Measure weights using uniform non-standard units (whole and half)

Framework objectives

- *Estimate, measure, weigh and compare objects choosing and using suitable uniform non-standard or standard units and measuring instruments, (e.g. a lever balance, metre stick or measuring jug)*
- Answer a question by selecting and using suitable equipment, and sorting information, shapes or objects; display results using tables and pictures

Teacher notes

Preparation
Photocopy PCM 29, one copy per pair. If you have time, photocopy PCM 30, one copy per pair.

Getting started
Ask each pair to choose a ball. Pass the chosen balls around. Children suggest which might be the heaviest and which might be the lightest. Record ideas to refer to later. In pairs, children discuss and agree an estimate of how many felt pens, cubes, pegs and coins their ball weighs. Make sure children understand the word estimate.

Activity
Children discuss in pairs and estimate how many of each item they will need to balance their ball, recording their estimates on PCM 29. Also record the item used to weigh the ball. They might find it helpful to hold the ball in one hand and a felt pen, cube, peg or coin in the other hand to support their estimates. Each pair uses the items to weigh their ball and record the result on the PCM. They discuss how close their estimates were to the actual weights.
Children then work in a group to compare all the balls. They agree which is heaviest and which is lightest and arrange the balls in order of weight.

Extra help
Support the estimates of the number of items needed to balance the ball. *Are cubes heavier than coins? Does that mean we'll need more or less of them?* If the first weighing shows that the estimates are significantly different to the result, encourage children to review their estimates. Repeat at a later stage if necessary.

Further extension
Once the children have ordered the balls by weight, ask them to compare size too. Discuss what they notice, and why each ball might be better for playing a particular game.

If you have time
Children choose a different object to weigh and draw it on PCM 30. They estimate and then weigh the object using the same units of weight as in the main activity and compare their chosen object to the ball.
Alternatively, remind children that a ball is a sphere. Ask them to collect spheres from around the room and order them from the lightest to the heaviest. Show them how to use the balance to check their order is correct.

Be aware

- Children might assume that smaller items are lighter and that they will need more of the smaller items. Encourage them to weigh each item in their hands to help check this. Real coins may be smaller but heavier than one or more of the other items.

Outcomes

- I can weigh a ball using four different items.
- I can use my results to put the balls in order from lightest to heaviest.

Supporting resources

- A range of spherical objects such as marbles, beads and the spheres from sets of blocks or 3D shapes.

Challenge Plan: Year 1

C2: comparing weights; measuring weights; reading the time to the hour; organising and interpreting information in tables

Summary

Y1 ⭐ **C2.2**

How much is a kilogram?

A small group working with an adult

Year 1 Challenge Workbook page 27

A balance and a 1 kg weight for each pair of children; four large, clear bags; four sticky labels; cubes; felt pens; real coins; pegs; digital camera (optional)

Abacus Evolve objectives

- **Y1** Estimate then measure weights, recording estimates
- **Y2** Estimate, measure and compare weights using standard units: kilograms, grams

Framework objectives

- *Estimate, measure, weigh and compare objects choosing and using suitable uniform non-standard or standard units and measuring instruments, (e.g. a lever balance, metre stick or measuring jug)*
- **Y2** Estimate, compare and measure lengths, weights and capacities, choosing and using standard units (m, cm, kg, litre) and suitable measuring instruments
- **Y2** Listen to others in class, ask relevant questions and follow instructions

Teacher notes

Preparation
Supply enough cubes, plastic or real coins, pegs and felt pens for children to weigh 1 kg of each. Alternatively use items of your choice. If you are using different items to those in the Workbook, cover the picture in the book with a sticky label for children to draw or write the name of the item. Provide sticky labels for children to label the bags.

Getting started
Show children the 1 kg weight. *This is what we use to measure weight with when we want to use a standard measure recognised all over the world. Pass the weight around. Do you think it is heavy or light?*

Activity
Children work from Workbook page 27. They discuss and estimate how many of each item will balance the 1 kg weight, and record their estimates on the workbook page. Encourage children hold the weight in one hand and a felt pen, cube, peg or coin in the other hand to support their estimates. The group decide which pair will work with each type of item. Pairs take turns to balance the 1 kg weight with their item. After counting, each pair puts their items in a bag and labels it. Everyone records their results in their workbook. When all the weighing is complete, children compare their results. Ask them to arrange the four bags in order of size, from smallest to largest bag. Now put the bags in order of number of items. *Is the order the same? If not, why might that be?*

Extra help
Do the scales balance? Try one more/one less. Are cubes heavier than coins? Will we need more or less?

Further extension
Children weigh one of each item against one of the others and order them by weight, from lightest to heaviest, and discuss what they find out. *How could using different combinations of coins change the results?*

If you have time
Photograph each bag. Children arrange the photos in order of size (by look or by number) with the caption *1 kg*.

Be aware

- If children haven't used real coins for some time, they are likely to be distracted by them. You may prefer to use plastic coins, if you have enough.
- Talk to children about working safely with weights.

Outcomes

- I can weigh out 1 kilogram of different objects.
- I know that the size of an object doesn't tell me how heavy it is.

Supporting resources

- A range of weights to experiment with.

C2: comparing weights; measuring weights; reading the time to the hour; organising and interpreting information in tables

Summary

Y1 ⬡ **C2.3**

How much is a gram?

Groups working independently

Year 1 Challenge Workbook page 28

Year 1 Challenge PCM 31 (optional)

A balance and a 1 g weight for each pair of children; four small, clear bags; four sticky labels; paper clips; grains of rice; feathers; cotton wool balls; digital camera (optional)

Abacus Evolve objectives

- **Y2** Estimate, measure and compare weights using standard units: kilograms, grams
- **Y2** Begin to recognise the relationship between grams and kilograms

Framework objectives

- **Y2** Estimate, compare and measure lengths, weights and capacities, choosing and using standard units (m, cm, kg, litre) and suitable measuring instruments
- **Y2** Listen to others in class, ask relevant questions and follow instructions

Teacher notes

Preparation
If you do not have any 1 g weights or sufficiently light items, use 5 g weights. The children will still get the idea that grams are much smaller than kilograms. If you are using different items to those shown in the Workbook, cover the picture in the book with a sticky label for children to draw or write the name of the item. Provide sticky labels for children to label the bags.

Getting started
Show the children the 1 g weight and explain that this is what we use to weigh small items with when we want to use a standard measure recognised all over the world. Pass the weight around the group and ask the children whether they think it is heavy or light.

Activity
Children work from Workbook page 28. They discuss and estimate how many of each item they will need to balance the 1 g weight and record their estimate in their workbook. Encourage children to handle the 1 g weight and the items they are going to use to balance it. They might find it helpful to hold the weight in one hand and a paper clip, feather, grain of rice or cotton wool ball in the other hand to support their estimates. Children take turns to balance the 1 g weight with one type of item. One pair of children could count those items while another pair carries out the next weighing. After counting, the pair of children place the items in a small bag and label it. Everyone records their results in their workbook.
When all the weighing is complete, children compare their results. They arrange the bags in order of size, from the smallest to the largest, then put the bags in order of number of items. *Is the order the same? If not, why might that be?* Ask children to share their ideas.

Further extension
Weigh one of each item against one of the others and order them by weight, from the lightest to the heaviest. *Does this order match the order of the bags, when ordered by number of objects?* Compare the 1 kg and 1 g bags.
Which items in the classroom would you measure in grams? Which items would you measure in kilograms? Children can record their ideas on PCM 31.

If you have time
Photograph each bag separately. Print out sufficient copies of the pictures for children to stick in their class books in order of size (either by look or by number) with the caption *1 g*.

Be aware

- 1 g is very light. Check the items children are going to use are light enough to compare with 1 g.

Outcomes

- I can weigh 1 g of different items.
- I know the difference between a gram and a kilogram.

Challenge Plan: Year 1

C2: comparing weights; measuring weights; reading the time to the hour; organising and interpreting information in tables

---

Summary

Y1 ⭐ C2.4

Analogue and digital pelmanism

A small group working with an adult

Year 1 Challenge PCMs 32 and 33

Thin card; scissors; large analogue clock; large digital clock; small analogue and digital clocks for each child (optional)

Abacus Evolve objectives

- Read the time to the hour on analogue clocks
- **Y2** Read the time to the hour and half hour on analogue and 12-hour digital clocks

Framework objectives

- Use vocabulary related to time; order days of the week and months; read the time to the hour and half hour
- **Y2** *Use units of time (seconds, minutes, hours, days) and know the relationships between them; read the time to the quarter hour; identify time intervals, including those that cross the hour*

Teacher notes

Preparation

Photocopy PCMs 32 and 33 onto thin card, one copy of each per pair. Cut out the clock cards. If possible, use different coloured card for each pair, to prevent sets of cards getting mixed up.

Activity

- Explain that clocks come in two kinds, analogue and digital. Tell children that they can read o'clock times on one kind of clock and you are going to show them how to read the same times on digital clocks.
- Explain that digital clocks show the time in a different way. *The first two digits tell you which hour it is, the same as the short hand on an analogue clock. The last two digits tell you how many minutes past the hour, just like the long hand on an analogue clock. O'clock means no minutes past the hour, so the two digits are always zero for o'clock.*
- Ask children to show you random o'clock times on both types of clock. When you are happy that they understand, move on to the activity.
- Show children the analogue and digital clock cards. Give each pair their set of 24 cards. Show them how to set them out in a 6 by 4 grid, face down. Explain that they are looking for matching pairs which tell the same time. One will be analogue and the other digital.
- Show children how to pick two cards and turn them over. If the cards match, the player can keep them. If they don't, then they turn them face down again.
- Explain that they need to try to remember where each time was so that they can collect as many matching pairs as possible. The winner is the player who has collected the most pairs when they have all been found.

Extra help

When the first of a pair of cards is turned over, check that the child knows what the partner clock looks like. Ask them to show the matching time on the other type of clock. Support as necessary. Ask questions to jog their memories. *Now where was that 2 o'clock? I know it was over here somewhere!*

If you have time

Shuffle one set of cards and deal them equally to children. Use them to play 'O'clock snap'.

Mix children up so they play the pelmanism game with a new partner.

Be aware

- Children are often more familiar with digital clocks today and may need more support with reading analogue times. It is not necessary for them to use the words analogue and digital.

Outcomes

- I can read o'clock times on analogue and digital clocks.

Supporting resources

- Show the children how to play 'What's the time Mr Wolf' at playtime.
- Read time rhymes and stories such as Hickory Dickory Dock (in any good nursery rhyme book) and *Tom and the Tinful of Trouble* by Nick Sharratt and Stephen Tucker, published by Scholastic (ISBN 978-0-439944-74-9).

Challenge Plan: Year 1

C2: comparing weights; measuring weights; reading the time to the hour; organising and interpreting information in tables

Summary

Y1 ⭐ C2.5

Coin pictogram

Pairs working independently

Year 1 Challenge PCM 34

A bag containing 1p, 2p, 5p, 10p and 20p coins for each pair

Abacus Evolve objectives

- Organise information in simple lists, tables, pictograms or block graphs
- Interpret information from simple lists, tables, pictograms or block graphs
- Sort and organise information using objects or pictures

Framework objectives

- *Answer a question by recording information in lists and tables; present outcomes using practical resources, pictures, block graphs or pictograms*
- Use diagrams to sort objects into groups according to a given criterion; suggest a different criterion for grouping the same objects
- Answer a question by selecting and using suitable equipment, and sorting information, shapes or objects; display results using tables and pictures
- Ask and answer questions, make relevant contributions, offer suggestions and take turns

Teacher notes

Preparation
Photocopy PCM 34, one copy per pair.
Prepare a small bag of coins for each pair. Use 1p, 2p, 5p, 10p and 20p coins only, with no more than six of any particular coin.

Getting started
Give each pair a bag of coins and explain that they are going to sort them out. Explain that it will be difficult to remember how many of each type there are. *It will be much easier to draw them on a pictogram.* Give each pair PCM 34 and explain how to complete it.

Activity
Pairs sort their coins into piles according to value. They should deal with one type of coin at a time. They then draw round each coin in the appropriate square of the pictogram, until they have completed the graph.
Pairs then discuss their pictograms and ask each other questions about them.

Extra help
If children find it hard to keep track of which coins they have drawn, encourage them to sort all the coins onto the pictogram first, then remove each coin as they draw around it.

Further extension
Which pair in the group has the most money? How could you use the pictograms to work it out? Scaffold them with comments such as: *Tom and Asha only have one 20p coin, but they have lots of 10p coins, more than anyone else. Zina and Koby have three 20p coins but no 10p coins.*

If you have time
Ask pairs to work out how much money they have in total. They can find the total of each line of coins, then add the five totals together. Alternatively, scaffold them as they count the whole bagful by counting on.

Be aware

- Real coins seem to be far more attractive than plastic ones. If children are likely to be distracted by real coins, use plastic ones.

Outcomes

- I can make a pictogram.
- I can use a pictogram to find out information.

Supporting resources

- A small piece of tack to hold each coin in place until it is dealt with can be a great help.

Challenge Plan: Year 1

C2: comparing weights; measuring weights; reading the time to the hour; organising and interpreting information in tables

Summary

Y1 ⬡ **C2.6**

Favourite colours

Individuals or pairs working independently

Year 1 Challenge Workbook page 29

Blue, red, yellow and green cubes (optional)

Abacus Evolve objectives

- Organise information in simple lists, tables, pictograms or block graphs
- Interpret information from simple lists, tables, pictograms or block graphs
- Sort and organise information using objects or pictures

Framework objectives

- *Answer a question by recording information in lists and tables; present outcomes using practical resources, pictures, block graphs or pictograms*
- Use diagrams to sort objects into groups according to a given criterion; suggest a different criterion for grouping the same objects
- Describe a puzzle or problem using numbers, practical materials and diagrams; use these to solve the problem and set the solution in the original context

Teacher notes

Getting started
Ask each child to open Workbook page 29. Look at the pictures and speech bubbles together. *This class have been asked to say their favourite colour.* Check that children can read each bubble. If necessary, go through each speech bubble with the group and support them to underline each colour name.
What is the most popular colour in the class? It's not easy to tell from all these bits of information. You are going to build a picture, a graph, of Class 1B's favourite colours. This will make it easier to read the information. Explain how to complete the graph. Check that children can read the questions at the bottom of the sheet.

Activity
Children work in pairs or individually to complete the block graph. They answer the questions.

Extra help
If children get lost when transferring the information to the block graph, suggest that they tick each speech bubble as they put that information on the graph. They could also select matching cubes for the information and discard them once they have coloured the matching square.
Support reading the graph questions if necessary.

Further extension
Ask children to collect favourite colours from the group and redraw the block graph. *Do the answers to the questions change?* They could add any new colours next to the others.

If you have time
Children could compare their graph with other children. *Are they the same?* They should be since they have the same information, so if not, can they find the mistake?

Be aware

- Children may need reminding to colour the block graph squares from the bottom up.

Outcomes

- I can put information into a block graph.
- I can read a block graph.

Supporting resources

- Read 'The Pet Graph' in *Poems to Count on* by Sandra Liatsos, published by Scholastic (ISBN 978-0-590636-77-4).

D2: names of 3D shapes; features of 3D shapes; add by counting on; add two multiples of 10

Summary

Y1 ☆ D2.1		**Spot the 3D shapes**
		Pairs working independently
		Year 1 Challenge Workbook page 30
		Counters; dice; interlocking cubes; 3D shapes

Abacus Evolve objectives

- Begin to use the names of common 3D shapes: cube, cuboid, cylinder, sphere, cone, pyramid
- Begin to relate solid shapes to pictures of them

Framework objectives

- *Visualise and name common 2D shapes and 3D solids and describe their features; use them to make patterns, pictures and models*
- Ask and answer questions, make relevant contributions, offer suggestions and take turns

Teacher notes

Preparation
Collect 3D shapes: cube, cuboid, triangular prism, cylinder, sphere.

Getting started
Explain to the children that they are going to play a game to spot the 3D shapes. Explain how the game works.

Activity
Children work from Workbook page 30. Each child chooses a counter (use 3D shapes if you have them), and places it on Start. They take turns to roll the dice and move their counter that number of spaces. If they land on a picture of a 3D shape and name it correctly, they collect an interlocking cube. They continue taking turns until one person lands on the shape robot – they are the winner.

Extra help
Draw or print out pictures of different cubes and cuboids. Stick these over the top of the other 3D shapes on the workbook pages. This will allow children to focus only on these two 3D shapes.

Further extension
Investigate how many interlocking cubes you need to make bigger cubes. The first cube you can make needs eight interlocking cubes. How many cubes do you need to make a cube which is bigger than that?

If you have time
What other shapes can you make with interlocking cubes?

Be aware

- 3D shapes become 2D shapes as soon as they are in a picture. However, understanding a 2D representation of a 3D shape is important.

Outcomes

- I can recognise 3D objects from their pictures.
- I can follow instructions.

Supporting resources

- Explore different mathematical conventions for showing 3D shapes in books or posters.
- Use an interactive whiteboard to demonstrate different ways of representing 3D shapes.
- Use http://www.teachers.ash.org.au/jeather/maths/dictionary.html to explore different shapes and how they are drawn.

D2: names of 3D shapes; features of 3D shapes; add by counting on; add two multiples of 10

Summary

Y1 ⭐ D2.2 **Making dice**

A group of six children working with an adult

Year 1 Challenge PCMs 35 and 36

Thin card; scissors; A3 paper or card; a collection of dice in different shapes; sticky labels; counters; 3D shapes: cube, cuboid, triangular prism, cylinder, sphere

Abacus Evolve objectives

- Begin to use the names of common 3D shapes: cube, cuboid, cylinder, sphere, cone, pyramid
- Describe features of familiar 3D shapes: number, shapes and types of faces

Framework objectives

- *Visualise and name common 2D shapes and 3D solids and describe their features; use them to make patterns, pictures and models*
- *Take turns to speak, listen to others' suggestions and talk about what they are going to do*

Teacher notes

Preparation
Photocopy PCM 35, and cut out the flash cards. Collect the following 3D shapes: cube, cuboid, triangular prism, cylinder, sphere. Photocopy PCM 36, preferably enlarged to A3.

Activity
- Ask children to sort the 3D shapes, allowing them to decide on the categories. Encourage them to explain their reasons for sorting them in that way.
- Rehearse shape words using the flash cards on PCM 35: *face, triangle, rectangle, circle, square*.
- Show children the collection of dice. *What shape are the dice? Why do you think they are these shapes? What is on the face of each dice? Do any numbers appear more than once?*
- *You are going to make a dice.* Ask each pair to choose one of the 3D shapes and explain their choice to the group. Encourage the group to listen to the explanations. *Is there another shape that you think would make a better dice? Why?*
- Children make their dice, using sticky labels to add the numbers. Remind them that they must only stick one number on each face, and they should not repeat any numbers.
- Give each pair a chance to showcase their dice, explain what is good about it and demonstrate how it works. *How many different numbers can you throw? Is this important when playing games with dice?*
- *We are going to play a game using one of the dice we have made.* Show children the game board on PCM 36. *The aim is to be the first to reach the finish!* Encourage children to work together to decide a context for the game and decorate the game board by adding pictures and words. *Which dice will you use? Why?* Give each team of two or three a coloured counter and let them play the game. *Did you choose the right dice? Would you like to choose a different one? Why?* Let children play again using a different dice if they like.

Extra help
Only include cube-shaped dice numbered 1 to 6 in the collection.

Further extension
What makes a good dice? Which shapes have faces that are all the same size? Would they make good dice? How many numbers could you fit on them if you are only allowed one number of each face? Children can make dice from everyday objects such as cereal boxes, match boxes, sweet tubes, etc. *Which dice are best? Why?*

If you have time
Make a new game that uses a 1–4 dice. *Which shape dice do we need?* Make one and play the game to test it.

Be aware

- You will need fair dice for this activity. Note that some manufactured dice with unequal faces or round dice are weighted and will not work here.

Outcomes

- I can ask relevant questions and follow instructions.
- I can explain my choices and decisions.

Supporting resources

Look up the names of the shapes in a maths dictionary or online:
- http://www.teachers.ash.org.au/jeather/maths/dictionary.html

Challenge Plan: Year 1

Summary

Y1 D2.3

The shape sorter

Pairs or groups working independently

Year 1 Challenge Workbook page 31

Year 1 Challenge PCM 37

A collection of everyday 3D objects: cubes, cuboids, spheres, cylinders

Abacus Evolve objectives

- Begin to use the names of common 3D shapes: cube, cuboid, cylinder, sphere, cone, pyramid
- Describe features of familiar 3D shapes: number, shapes and types of faces
- Begin to relate solid shapes to pictures of them

Framework objectives

- *Visualise and name common 2D shapes and 3D solids and describe their features; use them to make patterns, pictures and models*
- Describe simple patterns and relationships involving numbers or shapes; decide whether examples satisfy given conditions
- Ask and answer questions, make relevant contributions, offer suggestions and take turns

Teacher notes

Preparation
Make a collection of everyday 3D objects: cubes, cuboids, spheres and cylinders.

Getting started
Explain to children how to use the diagram in their books to sort the objects into their different shapes. Ask them to imagine that they are going to put all the objects into the shape sorter. The sorter will ask them questions to work out which shape each object is. Read through each of the questions with children.

Activity
Children work from Workbook page 31. They look at each object in the collection and answer the question *does it roll?* They answer *yes* or *no*, then follow the correct branch of the diagram. They answer the next question. *Is it a cylinder? Is it a cube?* This should lead them to a picture of the shape they are holding.
When they have finished sorting the shapes, they should talk together about how the shapes have been sorted. *Do the answers make sense? Do you want to change your mind?*

Extra help
Play 'guess my shape'. One person chooses a shape from the set without showing their partner. Their partner asks them *yes* or *no* questions to find out which shape they have chosen.

Further extension
Children make their own collection of shapes and use PCM 37 to create a diagram to sort them. When they have tried it out they could give the page to a friend and see if their diagram works.

If you have time
Children could play the 'yes/no' game. They ask their partner some questions about 3D shapes. Their partner has to try to answer all the questions without using the words *yes* or *no*. If they do say *yes* or *no*, the children swap roles.

Be aware

- Asking closed questions requires a specific skill, needed for sorting information.
- When deciding what makes a good question to sort information it is important to separate into groups of roughly equal size.

Outcomes

- I can recognise the features of some 3D shapes.
- I can name some 3D shapes.
- I can use a tree diagram to sort shapes.

Supporting resources

- Use a branching database to create branching databases that the children can use to sort shapes.
- Play the 'Mittens' game: http://primary.naace.co.uk/activities/sorting_games/index.htm

Summary

Y1 ◯ D2.4

Fill the box

A small group working with an adult

Year 1 Challenge PCMs 38 and 39

Thin card; scissors; glue; 1 cm cubes

Abacus Evolve objectives

- Add by counting on, not bridging a multiple of 10 other than 10 or 20

Framework objectives

- Relate addition to counting on; recognise that addition can be done in any order; use practical and informal written methods to support the addition of a 1-digit number or a multiple of 10 to a 1-digit or 2-digit number
- Describe ways of solving puzzles and problems, explaining choices and decisions orally or using pictures

Teacher notes

Preparation
Photocopy PCM 38 onto thin card, one copy per pair. Cut out the number cards and the net from each copy. Fold and glue each net to make a cuboid, leaving the top open like a lid.

Activity
- *We are going to play a game. Think carefully about how you can get better at winning this game.*
- The aim is to fill the box with 1 cm cubes – the person who puts the last cube into the box is the winner. Sort the number cards into 1s and 2s and place them in two piles, face up. Each child starts with eight cubes. They take turns to put one or two cubes into the box. If they add one cube, they take a '1' card and place it in front of them. If they add two cubes, they place a '2' card in front of them. *Who puts the last cube into the box?*
- Children play the game several times in pairs. As they play, ask these questions and discuss the answers.
  - *What do you notice about the number of cubes you are placing?*
  - *Does it help to record your moves in one game before playing the next game?*
  - *Is it possible to get better at this game? What do you think makes a difference?*
  - *Who is most likely to win? Does it matter who starts? Why?*
- Each pair discusses strategies for winning and explains their strategies to the group. The group test the strategies and discuss new ideas.

Extra help
Make a 2 × 2 × 2 box and play the same game. Each child starts with four cubes.

Further extension
Repeat the activity without the cubes and ask children to record what they are doing using PCM 39.

If you have time
Put all the cubes into the box and play the game in reverse. Each child takes turns to take either one or two cubes out of the box. The winner is the child who takes the last cube.

Information
The number of cubes that you choose decides which strategy will work best. For example, with a 12-cube box the critical numbers are 4, 6 and 9. Once you have put any of these numbers of cubes into the box, you can always win because you can always add either 1 or 2 to get to the next critical number and ultimately 12 cubes.

Be aware

- This activity is about developing strategic thinking. Children need to realise that it makes a difference who starts and if they choose 1 or 2. They may also realise that they should think more than one step ahead.

Outcomes

- I can add by counting on.
- I can make a strategy to win a game and explain it.

Supporting resources

- Play 'Got It' at http://nrich.maths.org/public/viewer.php?obj_id=1272. Change the target number to 12, and the maximum number to be added to 2. Children can test their strategies on the interactive white board or online

D2: names of 3D shapes; features of 3D shapes; add by counting on; add two multiples of 10

Summary

Y1 ⭐ D2.5

Four dice

Individuals or pairs working independently

Year 1 Challenge PCM 40

Four dice per child

Abacus Evolve objectives

- Add by counting on, not bridging a multiple of 10 other than 10 or 20

Framework objectives

- Relate addition to counting on; recognise that addition can be done in any order; use practical and informal written methods to support the addition of a 1-digit number or a multiple of 10 to a 1-digit or 2-digit number

Teacher notes

Preparation
Photocopy PCM 40, one copy per child.

Getting started
Explain to children that they are going to work on their own to solve some problems using dice. Then they are going to talk to a partner to check their workings.

Activity
Children work individually at first. They consider whether there are easy ways to add four dice numbers. They then throw four dice, record the numbers in the boxes on PCM 40, then find the total.

| 5 | 5 | 3 | 7 | Total 20 |

They repeat this several times.
Children swap sheets with a partner and mark each other's answers. They take turns to explain to each other what method they used to find the totals. They discuss other ways they could have done it.
Pairs discuss the lowest possible total of four dice numbers, and then the highest possible total.

Extra help
Use two dice instead of four and ask children to record the numbers in dots so that they can use them to help them to count.

Further extension
Use dice with larger numbers of faces, for example 12, to create different questions.

Be aware

- Using patterns on the dice to find doubles or pairs of numbers that add to 10 helps to calculate totals quickly.
- Children should be encouraged to count in 2s, 5s or 10s when possible, as it is more efficient than counting in 1s.

Outcomes

- I can add four small numbers by counting on.
- I can recognise doubles and pairs of numbers that add up to 10.

Supporting resources

Children can practise adding by solving the riddle 'As I was going to St Ives':
- http://www.rhymes.org.uk/as_i_was_going_to_st_ives.htm

Challenge Plan: Year 1

D2: names of 3D shapes; features of 3D shapes; add by counting on; add two multiples of 10

Summary

Y1 ⭐ **D2.6**

Apple packing

Pairs working independently

Year 1 Challenge Workbook pages 32–33

Year 1 Challenge PCMs 41 and 42

Green or red card

Abacus Evolve objectives

- Add two multiples of 10 by counting on in 10s

Framework objectives

- Relate addition to counting on; recognise that addition can be done in any order; use practical and informal written methods to support the addition of a 1-digit number or a multiple of 10 to a 1-digit or 2-digit number
- **Y2** Solve problems involving addition, subtraction, multiplication or division in contexts of numbers, measures or pounds and pence

Teacher notes

Preparation
Photocopy PCM 41, one copy per pair. Cut out the number cards. Make two copies of PCM 42, one green and one red. Cut out the bags of apple cards.

Getting started
Organise the children into pairs. Player 1 collects red apples and player 2 collects green apples. Each player places their bags of apples cards over each '10 apples' space on Workbook pages 32–33. Place the number cards face down. Explain the rules of the game to children.

Activity
This is a game for two players. Player 1 collects green apples and player 2 collects red apples. Player 1 turns over a number card. If the number is a multiple of 10, they pick up that many apples from their corresponding square on the game board. For example, if player 1 turns over a 20, they can pick up two bags of green apples and put them in their apple box. Children take turns until one child has collected 100 apples – they are the winner. Pairs keep an eye on the total number of apples in the box by adding up the numbers of apples from the uncovered squares. For example, if a child has uncovered four of their ten apples, then they have 40 apples in their box.

Extra help
Children can use number cards of the number 10 to support their understanding of multiples of 10.

Further extension
Ask children to keep a tally of the number of bags of apples they have put into the box. Write this number sentence: *If you have collected ___ bags of apples there are ___ apples in the box.* Ask each child to complete this number sentence as they put their bags of apples in the box.

If you have time
Set up a shop with the apple cards and sell the bags of apples for 10p each.
Sing *There were 10 in the bed and the little one said 'Roll over, roll over'*, but use multiples of 10 in the song. For example: *There were 50 in the bed and 10 fell out...*

Be aware

- Recognising the link between individual apples and a bag of 10 apples is important. Understanding that multiples of 10 relate to the number of bags of apples collected increases understanding of using 10s as a quick way of counting groups of 10 objects.

Outcomes

- I can count groups of 10 apples in 10s.
- I can recognise multiples of 10.

Challenge Plan: Year 1

E2: counting on and back in 10s; saying the number 1 or 10 more or less; subtracting TU − U; subtracting by counting back to a multiple of 10

Summary

Y1 ☆ E2.1

Caterpillars

Individuals or pairs working independently

Year 1 Challenge PCM 43

6-sided dice; 1–100 squares (optional)

Abacus Evolve objectives

- Count on and back in 10s from a 1-digit number
- Count on and back in 10s from any number up to 100

Framework objectives

- *Derive and recall all pairs of numbers with a total of 10 and addition facts for totals to at least 5; work out the corresponding subtraction facts*
- Solve problems involving counting, adding, subtracting, doubling or halving in the context of numbers, measures or money, for example to 'pay' and 'give change'
- Describe simple patterns and relationships involving numbers or shapes; decide whether examples satisfy given conditions

Teacher notes

Preparation
Photocopy PCM 43, one copy per child or pair.

Getting started
Show children PCM 43 and explain that the caterpillar at the top of the page has a number pattern written on it, but that some of the numbers are missing. Ask children to describe the rule that the number pattern follows, and explain how they worked it out.

Activity
Children work from PCM 43. They throw two 6-sided dice and add the numbers together. This is their start number, which they write on their caterpillar's head. The number on each segment of the caterpillar is 10 more than the one before. Children write the missing numbers on the remaining segments.

They then look at a caterpillar with just the final number shown. They must count back in 10s to fill in the missing numbers.

Extra help
If children are having problems adding 10 mentally, give them a 1–100 square, asking them if they can remember the quickest way of adding 10 using the grid (move down one square to the row below).

Further extension
Extend the number patterns beyond 100. You could do this by asking children to draw their own caterpillars with more segments, or by asking them to choose start numbers greater than 50.

If you have time
If each segment has 10 legs how many legs will each caterpillar have? Can you find a short way of working this out for each caterpillar? Explain to a friend how you know the answer.

Be aware

- Counting in 10s from numbers other than 0 can be a challenge, so plenty of practice counting on and back in 10s from any number is helpful.

Outcomes

- I can count on and back in 10s from a 1- or 2-digit number.

Supporting resources

Laminated copies of the caterpillars from PCM 43, together with dry erase markers, would be a useful resource for the Challenge corner.

E2: counting on and back in 10s; saying the number 1 or 10 more or less; subtracting TU − U; subtracting by counting back to a multiple of 10

Summary

Y1 ⭐ E2.2

Counter act

A small group working with an adult

Playing cards; coins with +10 on one side and +1 on the other; calculators; dice (optional); coins with +1 on one side and −1 on the other (optional)

Abacus Evolve objectives

- Count on and back in 1s or 10s up to 100
- Say the number that is 1 or 10 more or less than a given number

Framework objectives

- *Derive and recall all pairs of numbers with a total of 10 and addition facts for totals to at least 5; work out the corresponding subtraction facts*
- Say the number that is 1 more or less than any given number and 10 more or less for multiples of 10
- Listen to and follow instructions accurately, asking for help and clarification if necessary

Teacher notes

Preparation
From a pack of playing cards, remove the joker and the royal cards, leaving just the numeral cards up to 10; ace counts as 1. Make some cardboard coins with +10 on one side and +1 on the other, or stick labels onto real coins.

Activity
- Give out one calculator per pair. Show children how to enter numbers and use the +, − and = keys. Show them how they can repeat the last instruction by pressing the = key a second time.
- *We are going to practise counting on in 1s or 10s from any number.* These are the rules of the game.
  - Shuffle the playing cards and deal them out so that each pair has roughly the same number.
  - Child A draws two cards from the pack and adds them together, for example 5 + 8 = 13. This is the start number.
  - Child A tosses the coin to find out whether to count on in 1s or 10s.
  - Child B enters the start number on the calculator followed by +1 or +10. They enter =.
  - Child A and child B take turns to press = on the calculator, to add 1 or 10 repeatedly, until they pass 100.
  - When they pass 100, they stop. They then use the calculator to count back again in the same interval. They stop when they reach their start number.
  - Children then swap roles and repeat.
- Ask children to play the game in pairs.

Extra help
Use two 6-sided dice to set the starting number, and use a coin with +1 on one side and −1 on the other.

Further extension
Ask children to use the calculator to repeatedly subtract 1 or 10 from the starting number, and explore what happens when they go past 0.

If you have time
Challenge children to invent their own calculator games to play in pairs.

Be aware

- Some children find it difficult to read the numbers on a calculator. You may find it helpful to practise writing 'digital' numbers using straight lines.
- Using a calculator is an important skill but is not the focus of this activity. The calculator in this activity is used as a way of introducing different contexts for recognising familiar numbers.

Outcomes

- I can count on and back in 1s and 10s up to 100.

Supporting resources

Children could solve this calculator problem:
- http://nrich.maths.org/public/viewer.php?obj_id=184

Challenge Plan: Year 1

E2: counting on and back in 10s; saying the number 1 or 10 more or less; subtracting TU − U; subtracting by counting back to a multiple of 10

Summary

Y1 ⭐ E2.3

Choosing tracks

Pairs or groups working independently

Year 1 Workbook page 34

Year 1 Challenge PCM 44

Counters

Abacus Evolve objectives

- Count on and back in 1s or 10s up to 100
- Say the number that is 1 or 10 more or less than a given number

Framework objectives

- *Derive and recall all pairs of numbers with a total of 10 and addition facts for totals to at least 5; work out the corresponding subtraction facts*
- Say the number that is 1 more or less than any given number and 10 more or less for multiples of 10
- Listen to and follow instructions accurately, asking for help and clarification if necessary

Teacher notes

Preparation
Photocopy PCM 44, two or more copies per pair or group of three.

Getting started
Look at the Workbook page 34. Explain the rules of the game.

Activity
Children work from Workbook page 34. They play the game in pairs or threes. These are the rules.
- Each child places their counter on a different red number.
- They take turns to move their counter one space towards the centre of the board.
- For each move, children work out whether the number has changed by +1, +10, −1 or −10. They record this on the scoreboard on PCM 44. For example, a player who starts on 31 and moves to 21 will write −10.
- When they reach 9 in the centre of the board, they may choose which track to follow. They may not go back the way they came, and they may not choose the same track as another player.
- The game ends when all players have crossed the board and reached another red number.
- Each child works out their total score. One way is to count on from 0, counting the +10s first, and then the +1s. Children then count back, counting the −10s and finally the −1s.
- The winner of the game is the person with the largest total score.
Once children have played the game once, they are encouraged to explore whether going last affects a player's chances of winning. They should play again using a second copy of PCM 44 to record their scores.

Extra help
Draw a new version of the game board which uses only 1 more and 1 less.

Further extension
Draw a new version of the game board which uses 1, 10 and 100 more and less.

If you have time
Ask groups to create their own game involving counting on or back in 1s or 10s. Ask children to write a set of instructions to explain how to play it and then swap games in groups.

Be aware

- Some children find it difficult to adjust to counting from a different starting place.
- Using 1 more and 1 less and 10 more and 10 less can be confusing for children. Limiting the number of options by using only more or less will help.

Outcomes

- I can say whether a number has changed by +1, +10, −1 or −10.

Challenge Plan: Year 1

E2: counting on and back in 10s; saying the number 1 or 10 more or less; subtracting TU − U; subtracting by counting back to a multiple of 10

Summary

Y1 ⭐ **E2.4**

Take-away menu

Pairs working independently

Year 1 Challenge PCM 45

A menu from a take-away restaurant (optional)

Abacus Evolve objectives

- Begin to subtract a 1-digit number from a 2-digit number by counting back, not crossing 10
- Subtract by counting back to a multiple of 10
- Relate addition facts for pairs of numbers to an understanding of addition, including use of +, −, = and missing numbers
- Solve 'real-life' problems involving money (change)

Framework objectives

- Understand subtraction as 'take away' and find a 'difference' by counting up; use practical and informal written methods to support the subtraction of a 1-digit number from a 1-digit or 2-digit number and a multiple of 10 from a 2-digit number
- *Use the vocabulary related to addition and subtraction and symbols to describe and record addition and subtraction number sentences*
- Solve problems involving counting, adding, subtracting, doubling or halving in the context of numbers, measures or money, for example to 'pay' and 'give change'
- Ask and answer questions, make relevant contributions, offer suggestions and take turns

Teacher notes

Preparation
Photocopy PCM 45, one copy per child or pair.

Getting started
Show the take-away menu on the PCM. Ask children to work out how much chicken curry would cost on its own, without rice. Ask them to explain how they worked out the answer. Model how to record the calculation, for example *36p − 6p = 30p*. Read through the questions on the sheet together, ensuring children understand what they need to do.

Activity
Children work from PCM 45. They find the cost of three orders. The orders do not match the items on the menu exactly, so children will have to apply their knowledge of subtraction to work out the answers. Children are then challenged to make up their own problems for a partner to solve. Because children are making these problems up themselves, they may not all involve subtraction.

Extra help
Make a different version of the menu, with prices no greater than 20p.

Further extension
Make a different version of the menu, with prices greater than 50p. Alternatively, ask children to work out the bill for several friends paying for their orders together.

If you have time
Look at a real take-away menu and choose a meal. *How much would it cost?*

Be aware

- Using subtraction and addition to calculate in practical situations helps children to be able to use and apply their skills in a wide variety of situations.

Outcomes

- I can solve problems using subtraction.

Challenge Plan: Year 1

E2: counting on and back in 10s; saying the number 1 or 10 more or less; subtracting TU − U; subtracting by counting back to a multiple of 10

Summary

Y1 ☆ E2.5

Four in a line

A small group working with an adult

Year 1 Challenge Workbook page 35

6-sided dice; plenty of coloured counters in at least two colours

Abacus Evolve objectives

- Begin to subtract a 1-digit number from a 2-digit number by counting back, not crossing 10
- Subtract by counting back to a multiple of 10

Framework objectives

- Understand subtraction as 'take away' and find a 'difference' by counting up; use practical and informal written methods to support the subtraction of a 1-digit number from a 1-digit or 2-digit number and a multiple of 10 from a 2-digit number
- Describe ways of solving puzzles and problems, explaining choices and decisions orally or using pictures
- Explain their views to others in a small group, and decide how to report the group's views to the class

Teacher notes

Preparation
You may wish to prepare some extra game boards, similar to the one on Workbook page 35, but with numbers 51 to 100 (see 'Further extension' below).

Activity
- Look at Workbook page 35. Explain how to play the game in pairs.
  - Children choose a counter colour each and decide who will go first.
  - Child A throws the dice.
  - Child A places a counter in their colour over a number on the grid. (They cannot choose a number if it already has a counter on it.)
  - Child A subtracts the dice number from the grid number. If the answer to the subtraction is on the grid and is not already covered by a counter, child A places a counter on that number as well.
  - Child B has their turn.
  - Players take turns until one player gets four counters in a line (horizontal, vertical or diagonal).
- As children play, ask them to explain the choices they are making, both in terms of game strategies (choosing numbers to make their own line and/or interfering with their opponent's line) and in terms of calculation methods. Inevitably, some calculations will involve crossing tens boundaries, which children may not have encountered. They will therefore need to devise their own methods for doing this.

Extra help
Ask children to open two Workbooks to page 35. They can use one to play the game on, and they can use the other grid to help them to count on and back.

Further extension
Replace the 1 to 50 grid with a 51 to 100 grid. Children could also use two dice to play the game.

If you have time
Challenge children to develop their own 'Four in a line' grid game. Ask them to write instructions for their game and play it with a partner.

Be aware

- Subtracting by counting back is a useful strategy but children may need practice in counting back from any number.

Outcomes

- I can play a game involving subtracting numbers.

Supporting resources

Children could play online Connect 4:
- http://www.woodlands-junior.kent.sch.uk/Games/lengame/connect4.html

Challenge Plan: Year 1

E2: counting on and back in 10s; saying the number 1 or 10 more or less; subtracting TU − U; subtracting by counting back to a multiple of 10

Summary

Y1 ⭐ E2.6

Number lines

Pairs or groups working independently

Year 1 Challenge PCM 46

Coloured paper; rulers; scissors

Abacus Evolve objectives

- Subtract by counting back to a multiple of 10
- Subtract a 1-digit number from a 2-digit number by counting back, crossing 10

Framework objectives

- Understand subtraction as 'take away' and find a 'difference' by counting up; use practical and informal written methods to support the subtraction of a 1-digit number from a 1-digit or 2-digit number and a multiple of 10 from a 2-digit number
- Solve problems involving counting, adding, subtracting, doubling or halving in the context of numbers, measures or money, for example to 'pay' and 'give change'
- Describe ways of solving puzzles and problems, explaining choices and decisions orally or using pictures
- Ask and answer questions, make relevant contributions, offer suggestions and take turns

Teacher notes

Preparation
Photocopy PCM 46, one copy per pair or group of three. Cut out the word problems, pictures and number lines. If there will be more than one group sitting at a table, it may be useful to use different coloured paper.

Getting started
Give each pair or group of three all the cut-up sections of the PCM. Explain that they are going to match up the word problems, the pictures and the number lines.

Once groups have done this, they will move on to making their own versions of the activity. Give each child a sheet of coloured paper; give children in the same pair/group the same coloured paper. Explain that each child will write a word problem on their coloured paper and draw a number line to match. They will then cut up the separate parts. Each pair/group will shuffle their sections together in a pile and give them to another pair/group to match up.

Activity
Children match up the word problems, pictures and number lines from PCM 46.

Each child then makes up their own word story, and draws a number line to match it. Each pair/group puts all their sections together and gives them to another group. The groups then solve each other's problems.

Extra help
Initially, give children just the word problems and the pictures to match. Once they have done this, give them the number lines to match.

Further extension
For the second part of the activity, ask children to use three pieces of paper for each question: one for the word problem, one for the number line, and one for another way of solving the problem. Encourage them to draw diagrams instead of pictures.

Be aware

- Children can find it difficult to link words, pictures and numbers. Children who are good with numbers are sometimes challenged when asked to draw a diagram or picture, or to explain their answer. This activity is designed to support this development.

Outcomes

- I can use subtraction to solve problems.

A3: counting by grouping in 5s or 10s; adding a multiple of 10 to a 2-digit number; partitioning 2-digit numbers; ordering numbers

Summary

Y1 ⬡ A3.1	**Fingers and toes**
	A small group working with an adult
	Year 1 Challenge Workbook page 36
	Number cards, multiples of 5 up to 100; sticky notes; felt pens

Abacus Evolve objectives

- Count a number of objects by grouping in 5s or 10s

Framework objectives

- Solve practical problems that involve combining groups of 2, 5 or 10, or sharing into equal groups
- Describe simple patterns and relationships involving numbers or shapes; decide whether examples satisfy given conditions
- Take turns to speak, listen to others' suggestions and talk about what they are going to do

Teacher notes

Activity

- Ask children to sit in a circle and put their hands flat in front of them so that all five fingers on each hand can easily be seen.
- *How many fingers and thumbs can you see? How can we find out?* Children are likely to suggest counting 1s. Begin to count and make mistakes, forgetting where you got to and getting in a muddle. Suggest there must be a better way and you need children's help to find it.
- *How many fingers and thumbs are there on each hand?* Ask each child to count the fingers and thumb on one hand and label it with a sticky note (positioned so that the numbers are facing the child). *Do you notice anything about the numbers?* (They are all the same: 5.)
- Practise counting in 5s. Count along the hands in 5s, placing the matching number card next to each hand. Ask children what they notice about the numbers. (They all end in 5 or 0.)
- Children work from Workbook page 36. They estimate the number of fingers they can see in the picture, then find the total by counting in 5s.
- *How many are there in the classroom?* Children record an estimate in their Workbook. Encourage them to work in pairs and draw hands or numerals to support their investigation. *Does everyone agree?* If children have reached different totals, check if they included adults and anyone who left the room for a moment. Check by counting together in 5s and then in 10s, explaining why you could count in 10s (one person has 10 fingers).

Extra help

If children find it difficult to count in 5s, ask them how many fingers one person has. They can use their knowledge that 5 + 5 = 10 to count in fingers in 10s if they find this more straightforward. If necessary, support children with counting and recording numbers beyond 100.

Further extension

How many fingers are there in the classroom if we only count the fingers on people's left hands?

How many toes are there in the classroom if we only count the toes on people's right feet?

Be aware

- Children can often say numbers over 100 but are unsure of how to record them. Some children may write 120 as 10020. Support writing the relevant totals where necessary.

Outcomes

- I can count in 5s and 10s.

Supporting resources

Download 'Counting in 5s hands':
- http://www.sparklebox.co.uk/md/numbers/body.html

Challenge Plan: Year 1

A3: counting by grouping in 5s or 10s; adding a multiple of 10 to a 2-digit number; partitioning 2-digit numbers; ordering numbers

Summary

Y1 ⭐ A3.2

Fives

Pairs working independently

Year 1 Challenge PCM 47

Number cards, multiples of 5 up to 100; 0–100 number line (optional)

Abacus Evolve objectives

- Count a number of objects by grouping in 5s or 10s

Framework objectives

- Solve practical problems that involve combining groups of 2, 5 or 10, or sharing into equal groups
- Describe simple patterns and relationships involving numbers or shapes; decide whether examples satisfy given conditions
- Explain their views to others in a small group, and decide how to report the group's views to the class

Teacher notes

Getting started
Discuss counting fingers and toes in 5s. Show children the multiples of 5 number cards and practise counting up in 5s. Give each pair a set of the multiples of 5.

Activity
Children work from PCM 47. They colour the multiples of 5 on the 1–100 square. They then fill in the missing numbers (multiples of 5 ending in 5) on a 0–100 number line. Pairs then discuss what they notice about the patterns they can see and note down any observations.

Extra help
A labelled 0–100 number line will provide additional support for children who do not immediately recognise the multiples of 5. Children may find it easier to label the decade numbers on their number line first.

If you have time
Ask children to explain what they have noticed about the coloured numbers on the 1–100 square and the numbers they filled in on the number line. Count along the number line using the numbers in boxes only. *What am I counting in?* (10s)

Information
Open questions may help children think about the number patterns. They are counting on in 10s on the number line. You could model this by arranging children in a line, with hands outstretched. Ask the first person in the line to put one hand behind their back so that you count fingers by saying 5, 15, 25, …

Be aware

- Remember to count back as well as forward. Once you have counted all the fingers in the group, count back, supported by children hiding one hand at a time. Counting back often receives much less practice than it should.

Outcomes

- I can count in 5s and 10s.

Supporting resources

Download 'Counting in 5s hands':
- http://www.sparklebox.co.uk/md/numbers/body.html

A3: counting by grouping in 5s or 10s; adding a multiple of 10 to a 2-digit number; partitioning 2-digit numbers; ordering numbers

Summary

Y1 ☆ A3.3

Adding 10s game

Pairs working independently

Year 1 Challenge PCMs 48 and 49

6-sided dice; coloured pencils or counters; 0–100 number line or 1–100 square (optional)

Abacus Evolve objectives	Framework objectives
• Begin to add a multiple of 10 to a 2-digit number by counting on in 10s	• Relate addition to counting on; recognise that addition can be done in any order; use practical and informal written methods to support the addition of a 1-digit number or a multiple of 10 to a 1-digit or 2-digit number
	• Listen to and follow instructions accurately, asking for help if necessary

Teacher notes

Preparation
Photocopy PCMs 48 and 49, one copy of each per pair. Cut out the spinner from PCM 49 and add the pointer using a split pin.

Getting started
Provide each pair with two 6-sided dice. Show them the game board on PCM 48. Ask them to read some of the numbers. Show them how to roll the two dice and use them to make a 2-digit number. For example, if a 3 and a 6 are rolled, the child could make 36 or 63. Show them the spinner and demonstrate how to use it to determine whether to add 20, 30, 40 or 50 to their number. Explain that they then colour that number in their chosen colour on the game board (alternatively, children could use counters). *To win you must colour four numbers in a line – vertical, horizontal or diagonal.*

Activity
Children play the game in pairs. They take turns to roll two dice to make a 2-digit number, spin the spinner, and calculate their new number. They colour this number on the game board in their chosen colour. The winner is the first player to colour four squares in a line, vertically, horizontally or diagonally.

Extra help
A 0–100 number line or 1–100 square could be used to support addition.

Further extension
Ask children to work out the smallest and largest numbers they can make with the dice and spinner.

Information
The smallest number which can be made is *11 + 20 = 31*. The largest number is *66 + 50 = 116*.

Be aware	Outcomes
• There are a lot of variables in this game, so it may take some time for children to think about how to generate the numbers they want. If the game is taking too long, reduce the winning condition to three in a line (or three numbers on the same line).	• I can add a multiple of 10 to a 2-digit number.

Supporting resources

For a range of relevant resources (listed under 'Adding multiples and near multiples of 10') go to:
• http://www.primaryresources.co.uk/maths/mathsC1b.htm

Challenge Plan: Year 1

A3: counting by grouping in 5s or 10s; adding a multiple of 10 to a 2-digit number; partitioning 2-digit numbers; ordering numbers

Summary

Y1 A3.4

Work out my number

A small group working with an adult

Number cards 0–100; raffle tickets to 999 (optional)

Abacus Evolve objectives

- Begin to partition 2-digit numbers into T and U
- Recognise the value of each digit in a 'teens' number
- Recognise zero

Framework objectives

- *Read and write numerals from 0 to 20, then beyond; use knowledge of place value to position these numbers on a number track and number line*
- Describe simple patterns and relationships involving numbers or shapes; decide whether examples satisfy given conditions
- Ask and answer questions, make relevant contributions, offer suggestions and take turns

Teacher notes

Preparation
Shuffle the number cards 0–9 and 51–100 and set them aside. Shuffle the number cards 10–50.

Activity
- Deal six random cards (10–50). Read the numbers together. *How many tens in this number? How many units? What is the highest number of units shown on the cards? What is the lowest number of tens shown on the cards?*
- Explain that you have chosen one of the six numbers, and challenge children to work out which one. They may only do this by asking you if your number has a certain number of tens or units. Play the game together until the appropriate number is identified.
- Ask children to play the game in pairs: deal six random cards 10–50 to each pair; children take turns to choose a number from their six and answer questions about its tens and units until their partner guesses the number.
- As children become more confident, shuffle in the rest of the cards (0–9 and 51–100). Be ready to support pairs who are dealt a 1-digit number if necessary.

Extra help
If children are finding it hard to keep track of which numbers are left, suggest that they turn over a card when it is eliminated. Some children may find it helpful to order the numbers or group them in their own way, for example by putting together all the cards with the same number of tens or the same number of units.

Further extension
Use six raffle tickets up to 999 instead of number cards. Model how to ask questions about the hundreds digits.

If you have time
Ask children to help you to sort all the number cards into order.

Be aware

- Children may find it difficult to recognise that 1-digit numbers have zero tens, as the zero is implied, not shown. Support by helping to compare a 'teens' number with a 1-digit number which has the same number of units. Demonstrate making the two numbers using towers of 10 cubes and individual cubes if necessary.

Outcomes

- I can say how many tens and units there are in a 2-digit number.

Supporting resources

A 0–100 number line, with the decade numbers highlighted, may be helpful.

Challenge Plan: Year 1

A3: counting by grouping in 5s or 10s; adding a multiple of 10 to a 2-digit number; partitioning 2-digit numbers; ordering numbers

Summary

Y1 ⭐ A3.5

Who won the race?

Pairs working independently

Year 1 Challenge Workbook page 37

Abacus Evolve objectives

- Begin to partition 2-digit numbers into T and U
- Recognise the value of each digit in a 'teens' number

Framework objectives

- *Read and write numerals from 0 to 20, then beyond; use knowledge of place value to position these numbers on a number track and number line*
- Describe a puzzle or problem using numbers, practical materials and diagrams; use these to solve the problem and set the solution in the original context
- Ask and answer questions, make relevant contributions, offer suggestions and take turns

Teacher notes

Getting started
Look at the Workbook page. Read the numbers on the running vests together. *How many tens in this number? How many units in this number? How many tens does the number with 4 units have?* (6 tens)

Activity
Children work from Workbook page 37. In pairs they use the clues to identify and eliminate the numbers on the running vests, in order to find out who won the race.

Extra help
Remind children to cross out the numbers they have eliminated. If they make a mistake, suggest they start again, crossing out the numbers with a coloured pencil this time.

Further extension
Children could take turns to give their partner a number clue, for example: '*My number has 4 tens and 8 units*'. The partner writes the number for their friend to check. Extend to include numbers with hundreds.

Be aware

- Even when children are confident in reading and recognising numbers, they may remain unsure of what each digit represents. Reinforce this regularly by using a variety of representations.

Outcomes

- I can say how many tens and units there are in a 2-digit number.

Supporting resources

A 0–100 number line, with the decade numbers highlighted, may be helpful.

A3: counting by grouping in 5s or 10s; adding a multiple of 10 to a
2-digit number; partitioning 2-digit numbers; ordering numbers

Summary

Y1 ⬡ A3.6

In between

Individuals or pairs working independently

Year 1 Challenge Workbook page 38

0–100 number line (optional); number cards 0–100 (optional)

Abacus Evolve objectives	Framework objectives
• **Y2** Say a number lying between two numbers, up to at least 100	• **Y2** Order 2-digit numbers and position them on a number line; use the greater than (>), and less than (<) signs • **Y2** Describe patterns and relationships involving numbers or shapes, make predictions and test these with examples

Teacher notes

Getting started
Look at the Workbook page. Discuss the first sandwich: *How could you find the number between 7 and 9?* Suggest counting on from 7 if necessary. Extend children's thinking by asking questions such as: *What if the bottom slice of bread had number 10 on it? Which numbers could be in between then? Does it matter which one you write?*

Activity
Children work from Workbook page 38. They write a number that lies between each given pair of numbers.

Extra help
Children may find it helpful to have a 0–100 number line.

Further extension
Give each pair 20 cards from a set of number cards 0–100. Ask them to shuffle the cards and deal two, face up. Children take turns to say a number between the two numbers shown until they have named all the possibilities.
Repeat by dealing two more cards. Used cards should be placed on the bottom of the pack.
If the two numbers dealt are consecutive, children could either deal two new cards or, if they are familiar with mixed numbers, they could name a mixed number (e.g. $3\frac{1}{2}$) between the two consecutive numbers. When a pair of children have worked their way through their set of cards, they can swap with another pair.
Ask each pair to put their cards in order, and then put the ordered sets together.

Be aware	Outcomes
• Children can sometimes get confused over the meaning of 'between', and think that the two specified numbers are included.	• Children can sometimes get confused over the meaning of 'between', and think that the two specified numbers are included.

Supporting resources

There are some useful resources on comparing and ordering numbers at:
• http://www.primaryresources.co.uk/maths/mathsB5.htm

Challenge Plan: Year 1

B3: addition and subtraction facts up to 9; addition and subtraction facts up to 10; adding 1-digit to 2-digit numbers; finding a small difference

Summary

Y1 ✩ B3.1

Chasing 9

A small group working with an adult

Year 1 Challenge PCM 50

6-sided dice; dice with sides labelled 1–3 (optional)

Abacus Evolve objectives

- Know by heart addition and subtraction facts for pairs of numbers that total up to 9
- Know by heart addition and subtraction facts for pairs of numbers that total 10
- Begin to recognise that addition can be done in any order
- Record addition and subtraction facts for pairs of numbers that total up to 9, using +, − and = in number sentences

Framework objectives

- *Derive and recall all pairs of numbers with a total of 10 and addition facts for totals to at least 5; work out corresponding subtraction facts*
- Relate addition to counting on; recognise that addition can be done in any order; use practical and informal written methods to support the addition of a 1-digit number or a multiple of 10 to a 1-digit or 2-digit number
- *Use the vocabulary related to addition and subtraction and symbols to describe and record addition and subtraction number sentences*
- Listen with sustained concentration

Teacher notes

Preparation
Photocopy PCM 50, one copy per pair. Provide each pair with two dice.

Activity
- Explain the rules of the game.
  - Child A throws the two dice and finds the total. For example, he throws 2 and 4 and the total is 6.
  - Child A considers how close this is to 9. If child A is happy with his total, he writes it in the table on PCM 50, and records how far it is from 9. For example, −3.
  - If child A is not happy with his total, he can throw one or both of the dice again. For example, he keeps the 4 and re-throws the other dice. He throws a 6, giving him 4, 6 and a total of 10. Child A cannot choose to throw the dice again, so he must keep this score. He writes it in the table, and records how far it is from 9. For example, +1.
  - Child B then has her turn. The children continue for five turns each.
  - At the end of the game, they each add up their five scores. The player whose score is closest to 0 wins.
- Give each pair a copy of PCM 50 and two dice, and ask them to play the game.
- *Is this a game of chance? Do you have any strategies for winning the game? How can you decide what your chances are of throwing exactly 9? Can you make better decisions about when to throw the dice if you work out your chances each time?*

Extra help
Make the activity simpler by using dice labelled 1–3 and asking children to aim for a total of 6.

Further extension
Children can use three dice and on each turn they can choose to re-throw twice. *What happens to your chances of getting exactly 9 now?*

Information
Winning is more likely if children know the chances of throwing particular numbers. Children are unlikely to know the chances, but this is a good opportunity to discuss why children may decide to re-throw.

Be aware

- When finding their total, children are working with positive and negative numbers. It is not necessary to teach negative numbers in a formal way. Children should just focus on whether they are moving nearer or further away from 0 after their turn.

Outcomes

- I can record additions and subtractions using + and −.

Challenge Plan: Year 1

B3: addition and subtraction facts up to 9; addition and subtraction facts up to 10; adding 1-digit to 2-digit numbers; finding a small difference

Summary

Y1 ☆ B3.2

Numbers, words and pictures

Pairs working independently

Year 1 Challenge Workbook page 39

Year 1 Challenge PCM 51

Abacus Evolve objectives

- Know by heart addition and subtraction facts for pairs of numbers that total up to 9
- Record addition and subtraction facts for pairs of numbers that total up to 9, using +, − and = in number sentences
- Find totals of sets of coins

Framework objectives

- *Derive and recall all pairs of numbers with a total of 10 and addition facts for totals to at least 5; work out corresponding subtraction facts*
- *Use the vocabulary related to addition and subtraction and symbols to describe and record addition and subtraction number sentences*
- Solve practical problems that involve combining groups of 2, 5 or 10, or sharing into equal groups
- Solve problems involving counting, adding, subtracting, doubling or halving in the context of numbers, measures or money, for example to 'pay' and 'give change'
- Take turns to speak, listen to others' suggestions and talk about what they are going to do

Teacher notes

Preparation
Photocopy PCM 51, one copy per pair. Cut out the cards.

Getting started
Give each pair a set of cards. Ask children to match the number sentences on the cards to the pictures and words on the Workbook page. *Be careful: some questions may have more than one correct answer!*

Activity
Children work from Workbook page 39. They place the correct answer cards below the corresponding word problems.

Extra help
Start by giving children some pictures and number sentences to match together. Explain the context in words.

Further extension
Ask children to each make up a few number sentences and write them on small pieces of paper. Gather them all in, shuffle them, and deal them out to the children. Ask them to write a matching word problem for each of the number sentences they have been given. Ask children to swap with another child and pair up each other's number sentences and word problems.

Be aware

- For children to be good problem-solvers they need to be able to link number sentences to a context and a meaning. Linking words, pictures and numbers is a crucial part of making sense of a problem.

Outcomes

- I can use maths words and symbols to describe and write additions and subtractions.

Challenge Plan: Year 1

B3: addition and subtraction facts up to 9; addition and subtraction facts up to 10; adding 1-digit to 2-digit numbers; finding a small difference

Summary

Y1 ⬡ B3.3   **Countdown**

Pairs working independently

Year 1 Challenge Workbook page 40

Counters; 6-sided dice; dice with sides labelled + and − (optional)

Abacus Evolve objectives

- Know by heart addition and subtraction facts for pairs of numbers that total 10
- Record addition and subtraction facts for pairs of numbers that total 10, using +, − and = in number sentences
- Relate number bonds to an understanding of addition, including use of +, −, =

Framework objectives

- *Derive and recall all pairs of numbers with a total of 10 and addition facts for totals to at least 5; work out corresponding subtraction facts*
- *Use the vocabulary related to addition and subtraction and symbols to describe and record addition and subtraction number sentences*
- *Ask and answer questions, make relevant contributions, offer suggestions and take turns*

Teacher notes

Getting started
Look at the Workbook page. Explain the rules of the game.
- The aim is to get from 10 to 0.
- Each child places a counter on 10.
- Child A throws a dice.
- Child A chooses whether to add or subtract the dice number to or from the number they are on.
- Child A writes a number sentence to match, for example *10 − 2 = 8.*
- Child A moves their counter to their new position and writes their new number in the circle they land on.
- It is now child B's turn.
- Children take turns until one person reaches 0. If they go beyond 0, they have to start again from 10. If they go back too far and go beyond 10, they start again from 10.

Activity
Children work from Workbook page 40. They play the game in pairs, recording their number sentences on another piece of paper as they go.

Extra help
Rehearse number bonds to 5 and 10 to help with the calculations.

Further extension
Play the game again with a +/− dice to tell children whether to move backwards or forwards. Allow children to go beyond 0 and 10.

Be aware

- Relating their backward or forward movement to addition and subtraction is important in order for children to record their progress satisfactorily.

Outcomes

- I can write number sentences to show how I have moved forwards or backwards on the game board.

Challenge Plan: Year 1

B3: addition and subtraction facts up to 9; addition and subtraction facts up to 10; adding 1-digit to 2-digit numbers; finding a small difference

Summary

Y1 ◇ B3.4

Missing digits

A small group working with an adult

Year 1 Challenge PCM 52

Abacus Evolve objectives

- **Y2** Add by counting on in 1s from the larger number, crossing a multiple of 10
- **Y2** Add a 1-digit number to a 2-digit number, crossing a multiple of 10 (rehearse)
- **Y2** Add two 2-digit numbers using an appropriate strategy
- **Y2** Understand that subtraction is the inverse of addition, using missing number sentences
- **Y2** Know what each digit in a 2-digit number represents, including 0 as a place holder

Framework objectives

- **Y2** *Add or subtract mentally a single-digit number or a multiple of 10 to or from any 2-digit number; use practical and informal written methods to add and subtract 2-digit numbers*
- **Y2** *Understand that subtraction is the inverse of addition and vice versa; use this to derive and record related addition and subtraction number sentences*
- **Y2** *Identify and record the information or calculation needed to solve a puzzle or problem; carry out the steps or calculations and check the solution in the context of the problem*

Teacher notes

Preparation
Photocopy PCM 52, one copy per child.

Activity
- *You are going to solve some number problems. Each splodge is one digit. Find the missing digits.* Define 'digit' if necessary.
- Children work from PCM 52 in pairs. They use known number facts to find the missing digits in the first four number sentences.
- Discuss how children were able to find the answers.
- Children then find the missing digits in the second set of number sentences. These ones have more than one answer.
- *Show your answers to your partner. Are they different? Why?* Pairs note what they have found.
- Children make up missing-number sentences for their partner to solve. *Is there more than answer?*

Extra help
Fill in some digits on the PCM before you copy it so only one digit is missing in each number sentence.

Further extension
Give children some missing-number sentence problems that are impossible. For example, $19 - \square = 2\square$. Can children explain why they are unable to find an answer? Ask them to write their own impossible missing-number sentences.

If you have time
Play a number detective game with missing-number sentences. One child writes clues to the missing digits. Others decide if the problem can be solved, or what further information is needed to solve it.

Be aware

- Children often confuse digits and numbers, particularly as 1-digit numbers are both. Emphasise the importance of the place of a digit in a number.

Outcomes

- I can find the missing digits in an addition.

Supporting resources

Children can learn more about digits by playing this 2-digit number game:
- http://nrich.maths.org/public/viewer.php?obj_id=6343

Challenge Plan: Year 1

B3: addition and subtraction facts up to 9; addition and subtraction facts up to 10; adding 1-digit to 2-digit numbers; finding a small difference

Summary

Y1 ⬠ B3.5

Spotting ladybirds

Individuals or pairs working independently

Year 1 Challenge Workbook page 41

Abacus Evolve objectives

- Find a small difference between two numbers by counting on
- Know by heart doubles for numbers up to at least 5
- Begin to know by heart doubles for numbers up to at least 10
- Add by identifying near doubles for numbers up to 10

Framework objectives

- Understand subtraction as 'take away' and find a 'difference' by counting up; use practical and informal written methods to support the subtraction of a 1-digit number from a 1-digit or 2-digit number and a multiple of 10 from a 2-digit number
- Recall the doubles of all numbers to at least 10
- Describe simple patterns and relationships involving numbers or shapes; decide whether examples satisfy given conditions

Teacher notes

Getting started
Look at the ladybird on the Workbook page. *How many spots are on each wing?* Explain that the difference between the two wings is 1. (3 − 2).
You are going to draw spots on these ladybirds so that each one has a difference of 1 between the two wings. Make sure your ladybirds have no more than 10 spots. Discuss the fact that if they have already drawn a ladybird with three spots on the right wing and two spots on the left wing, they should not also draw a ladybird with two spots on the left wing and three spots on the right wing.

Make sure children realise that for the second set of ladybirds the wings should have a difference of 2.

Activity
Children work from Workbook page 41. They draw spots on the ladybirds to give a difference of 1 between each pair of wings. They then move on to making the ladybirds with a difference of 2 between wings.

Extra help
Ask children to draw ladybirds with up to 6 spots only.

Further extension
Children investigate how many ladybirds they can make with a difference of 3 spots between wings. They then move on to a difference of 4. They should think about what patterns they have noticed.

If you have time
Children can find out some statistics about ladybird spots. *Which is the most common number of spots?*

Be aware

- This activity requires systematic thinking to find all possibilities and to look for patterns in the answers. Children who understand how to find the difference may still need support to make sure they have found all possible solutions.

Outcomes

- I can find the difference between the number of spots on the wings of ladybirds.

B3: addition and subtraction facts up to 9; addition and subtraction facts up to 10; adding 1-digit to 2-digit numbers; finding a small difference

Summary

Y1 B3.6   **Investigating ladybirds**

Groups working independently

A1 paper; pens

Abacus Evolve objectives

- Know by heart addition and subtraction facts for pairs of numbers that total up to 9
- Know by heart addition and subtraction facts for pairs of numbers that total 10
- Find a small difference between two numbers by counting on

Framework objectives

- *Derive and recall all pairs of numbers with a total of 10 and addition facts for totals to at least 5; work out the corresponding subtraction facts*
- Understand subtraction as 'take away' and find a 'difference' by counting up; use practical and informal written methods to support the subtraction of a 1-digit number from a 1-digit or 2-digit number and a multiple of 10 from a 2-digit number
- Describe a puzzle or problem using numbers, practical materials and diagrams; use these to solve the problem and set the solution in the original context
- Take turns to speak, listen to others' suggestions and talk about what they are going to do

Teacher notes

Getting started
Give the group a sheet of A1 paper and some pens. *You are going to investigate how many different ladybirds you can make with any number of spots up to a total of 10. So your ladybirds can have a total of 10, 9, 8, 7, 6, 5, 4, 3, 2, 1 or 0 dots. How many possible ladybirds are there altogether? I would like you to record their work because I am interested in how you work it out.*

Discuss the fact that if they have already drawn a ladybird with three spots on the right wing and two spots on the left wing, they should not also draw a ladybird with two spots on the left wing and three spots on the right wing.

Activity
Children investigate how many ladybirds can be made with any number of spots between 0 and 10. They draw their ladybirds on the paper as they find them. Children should demonstrate that they are working systematically, for example by finding the ladybirds in order of total, starting with 0, or by using known number facts of pairs up to 10 to find each total of spots. Children may wish to progress from drawing the ladybirds to writing additions, for example *0 + 5, 1 + 4, 2 + 3*.

Extra help
Give children guidance on how to work systematically. Ask them to start by finding all the possible ways to make a total of 0, then move on to each total in order. You could ask them to investigate totals only up to 5.

Further extension
If you count a 1, 2 ladybird and a 2, 1 ladybird as two separate possibilities, how does this affect the total number of ladybirds?

Information
36 different ladybirds can be made if 'mirror images' are not allowed (for example 2 + 3 and 3 + 2).

66 different ladybirds can be made if 'mirror images' are allowed.

Be aware

- Children are not expected to use a table to show their working. The important thing is to develop a systematic approach and notice patterns.

Outcomes

- I can work carefully to find all the possibilities.
- I can find patterns in numbers.

Supporting resources

Children can practise counting ladybird dots and finding patterns here:
- http://nrich.maths.org/public/viewer.php?obj_id=1816

Challenge Plan: Year 1

C3: compare capacities; measure capacities using non-standard units; read the time to the hour and half hour; measure time in minutes

Summary

Y1 ⭐ C3.1

Spinner fun

Individuals or pairs working independently

Year 1 Challenge Workbook page 42

Paperclips; six identical bottles labelled empty, nearly 'empty', 'half empty', 'half full', 'nearly full', 'full' (optional); different sized containers

Abacus Evolve objectives

- Compare two or more capacities by direct comparison: pouring

Framework objectives

- *Estimate, measure, weigh and compare objects choosing and using suitable uniform non-standard or standard units and measuring instruments, (e.g. a lever balance, metre stick or measuring jug)*
- Describe ways of solving puzzles and problems, explaining choices and decisions orally or using pictures
- Listen to and follow instructions accurately, asking for help and clarification if necessary

Teacher notes

Getting started

Show children how to use the spinners on the Workbook page. Place one end of the paperclip over the centre point of a spinner, and position the point of a pencil on the centre point. Flick the end of the paperclip so that it spins around the circle.

Make sure children understand how to combine the results from the two spinners to colour and label the containers.

Activity

Children work from Workbook page 42. They use their spinners to find out how much of each cup to colour, for example half full, nearly empty, empty, etc. They write the one- or two-word description below each cup. They then think about how many different options can be generated from the two spinners. They write the number of options and explain how they worked it out.

Extra help

Label six identical bottles: 'empty', 'nearly empty', 'half empty', 'half full', 'nearly full' and 'full'. Fill them with appropriate quantities of coloured water. Leave the set of bottles on the table the children are working at for support.

Further extension

Show children how to use a measuring jug. Ask them to find several different sized containers. They pour water into the measuring jug up to a given point, for example 100 ml. They then pour this into the first container. They repeat for the other containers, pouring the same amount of water into each. Ask children to compare how full each container looks and explain what they see.

If you have time

Ask children to compare half empty and half full. *Are they the same?* Pour half of the contents of a full bottle into another identical bottle and compare with the labelled bottles used as extra help.

Are there any other words you could use to describe quantities?

Be aware

- Some children will be unable to recognise that half empty and half full are identical. Reinforce by joining two halves of shapes and real objects such as fruits and sandwiches to help development of the concept.

Outcomes

- I can colour a picture of a cup to show how full it is.
- I can work out how many different options can be made using two spinners.

Supporting resources

- Keep the set of filled and labelled bottles and add them to an interactive capacity display.

Challenge Plan: Year 1

C3: compare capacities; measure capacities using non-standard units; read the time to the hour and half hour; measure time in minutes

Summary

Y1 ⬡ C3.2

How much water in a puddle?

A small group working with an adult

Five containers with a clear increase in size, for example egg cup, mug, milk bottle, large jug and small bucket; access to water to fill the containers; access to the playground; a small whiteboard (optional); digital camera; 30 cm ruler (optional).

Abacus Evolve objectives

- Compare two or more capacities by direct comparison: pouring
- Begin to estimate then measure capacities, recording estimates
- Measure capacities using uniform non-standard units (whole and half)

Framework objectives

- *Estimate, measure, weigh and compare objects choosing and using suitable uniform non-standard or standard units and measuring instruments (e.g. a lever balance, metre stick or measuring jug)*
- Describe a puzzle or problem using numbers, practical materials and diagrams; use these to solve the problem and set the solution in the original context
- Take turns to speak, listen to each other's suggestions and talk about what they are going to do

Teacher notes

Preparation
Find five containers with a clear increase in size between each one. Fill them to the top with water. Take a photograph of each container. Find a suitable area in the playground (for example a small dip in the tarmac) and pour the contents of one of the containers onto the area to make a puddle. Ask a colleague to take a photograph of you pouring the water from the container.

Activity
- Bring children outside and show them the puddle but not the five containers. *How much water do you think is in the puddle?* You may need to start them off, for example *Could there be a teaspoonful?* Allow free discussion.
- Show children the five containers. Ask children to put them in order. *Which one do you think has just the right amount of water in to make another puddle the same as this one? How could we work this out?*
- You might like to record their ideas on a small whiteboard.
- Pour each container onto the playground, away from the original puddle. Photograph each new puddle.
- Look at each puddle. *Is it bigger or smaller than the first puddle?*
- Discuss with the group until they reach agreement on the likely container.
- Show children the photograph of you making the puddle to reveal who was right.

Extra help
Compare each new puddle with the original puddle. Keep returning to look at it after each pouring and look at the photograph, provided the viewing screen is not too small. Print off a copy of the photograph If you have time.

Further extension
Print out a set of photographs of each container and puddle for each child involved in the activity. Ask children to glue matching puddles and containers in their maths books or on coloured paper for display.

If you have time
If there is a tap nearby, explore making different sized puddles.

Be aware
- Photograph puddles with a 30 cm ruler in the picture for scale if the playground surface is uniform.

Outcomes
- I can order containers.
- I can estimate the amount of water in a puddle.

C3: compare capacities; measure capacities using non-standard units; read the time to the hour and half hour; measure time in minutes

Summary

Y1 ◇ C3.3

Rice mice game

Groups working independently

Year 1 Challenge PCM 53

Different coloured counters; a dice or spinner numbered 1–3; an eggcup; identical containers (for example plastic mugs); a large bowl; 2 kg of dried rice.

Abacus Evolve objectives

- Begin to estimate then measure capacities, recording estimates
- Measure capacities using uniform non-standard units (whole and half)

Framework objectives

- *Estimate, measure, weigh and compare objects choosing and using suitable uniform non-standard or standard units and measuring instruments (e.g. a lever balance, metre stick or measuring jug)*

Teacher notes

Preparation
Photocopy PCM 53, enlarged to A3 (you could laminate it if you intend to use it again).
Pour the rice into the bowl.
If you do not have a 1–3 dice, cover the 4, 5 and 6 on a normal dice with stickers and write 1, 2 or 3 as appropriate. Alternatively, use a 1–3 spinner.

Getting started
Show children the game board on PCM 53. Ask each child to choose a counter, and give them each an identical container, for example a mug. Put one mug alongside an eggcup. *How many eggcups of rice would fill the mug?* Record their estimates. *These are rice mice – they love rice! Every time your counter lands on a mouse, you can add an eggcup of rice to your container. If you land on a piece of cheese, you only get half an eggcup. This is because the mice won't want as much rice if they already have some cheese!*

Activity
All players place their counters on Start. Players decide between them who will go first.
Player 1 rolls a 1–3 dice. They move their counter that number of squares, choosing which path to follow.
If they land on a mouse, they fill the eggcup with rice and pour it into their mug. If they land on a piece of cheese, they half-fill the egg cup with rice and pour it into their mug. The other children must check that they have used the correct amount of rice.
Players take turns to move their counters. The winner is the first child to fill their mug to the top.
Children then estimate how many eggcups of rice are in each mug.
They measure by taking eggcups of rice out of the mugs and counting.

Further extension
At the end of the game, children who have not filled their mugs could estimate how many more eggcups of rice they would need to fill their mug. Check by adding egg cups until their mug is full. Were they right?

Information
Children may well try to pile up the rice when they fill the eggcup. However, they are unlikely to have a steady enough hand for this to make much difference to the outcome of the game. If you want to ensure there will be no disputes, show children how to level the surface of the rice by brushing a hand across the top of the eggcup.

Be aware

- Encourage children to be as tidy as possible but expect some rice to be spilt on the table and floor.

Outcomes

- I can estimate and check the capacity of one container using a smaller container.

Supporting resources

- Have other small containers to experience pouring from one container to another.

C3: compare capacities; measure capacities using non-standard units; read the time to the hour and half hour; measure time in minutes

Summary

Y1 ⬡ **C3.4**

Half past

A small group working with an adult

Year 1 Challenge PCM 54

Large and small card clock faces with moving hands; digital clock with flip-over numbers

Abacus Evolve objectives

- **Y2** Read the time to the hour and half hour on analogue and 12-hour digital clocks

Framework objectives

- **Y2** *Use units of time (seconds, minutes, hours, days) and know the relationships between them; read the time to the quarter hour; identify time intervals, including those that cross the hour*
- **Y2** *Listen to a talk by an adult, remember some specific points and identify what they have learned*

Teacher notes

Preparation
Photocopy PCM 54, one copy per child.

Activity
- *Clocks come in two kinds: analogue and digital. You already know how to read half-past times on analogue clocks, so now you're going to read the same times on digital clocks!*
- If necessary, remind children that the first two digits tell you which hour it is and the last two digits tell you how many minutes past the hour. *O'clock means no minutes past the hour, so the two digits are always zero for o'clock on a digital clock.* Ask children to show you random o'clock times on both types of clock.
- Give each child a clock face. Ask them to set the hands at 12 o'clock. Show them how to count in 5s as they move the hour hand around the clock. Check that they understand that one whole hour has passed. *There are 60 minutes in a whole hour.* Show them the smaller markings of one minute on the larger clock.
- Set the clock at a different o'clock time and count around the hour to reach 60 minutes again.
- Repeat the count but stop at half past. Remind children that the time they have stopped at is half past. *How many minutes have we reached? Half of 60 is 30, so halfway round the clock is 30 minutes.*
- Use a digital clock to show children how minutes are counted in digital time. Again, pause at half past and look at both clocks. Give children PCM 54 and ask them to complete the missing times.

Extra help
Help children to count around the clock in 5s until they reach half past. *Where is the hour hand when the minute hand reaches half past?* Support children to notice that the hour hand has also moved and is now half way to the next hour.

Further extension
Count in 5s around the clock face. Ask questions such as *is 20 minutes past 3 before or after half past 3? What about 40 minutes past? Tell me a time before half past 4. Tell me a time after half past 4.* Use the clock faces to support answering these questions.

Be aware

- Children often find it hard to coordinate moving one hand on a card clock while keeping the other hand still. Give a geared clock to children most likely to experience problems in this area.

Outcomes

- I can read half-past times on analogue and digital clocks.
- I know how many minutes there are in half an hour.

Supporting resources

- Have a range of clocks and timers to explore, including rocking tockers, sand timers and kitchen timers.
This weblink will allow you to show time advancing in minutes on both analogue and digital clocks:
- http://nationalstrategies.standards.dcsf.gov.uk/node/47764

Challenge Plan: Year 1

C3: compare capacities; measure capacities using non-standard units; read the time to the hour and half hour; measure time in minutes

Summary

Y1 ⬡ C3.5

How many minutes?

Individuals or pairs working independently

Year 1 Challenge Workbook page 43

Year 1 Challenge PCM 55

Scissors; glue; card clock faces and digital clocks (optional); number cards 0–60 (optional)

Abacus Evolve objectives

- Begin to use units to measure time: minutes
- Read the time to the hour and half hour on analogue clocks

Framework objectives

- Use vocabulary related to time; order days of the week and months; read the time to the hour and half hour
- Describe simple patterns and relationships involving numbers or shapes; decide whether examples satisfy given conditions

Teacher notes

Preparation
Photocopy PCM 55, one copy per pair. Cut out the number cards.

Getting started
Ask children to turn to Workbook page 43. Give each child a set of number cards containing all the multiples of 5 from 5 to 60. Explain that they will stick these cards on the workbook page to show the numbers of minutes past the hour.
How many minutes are there in half an hour? Ask children to point at half past on the clock. *Which number card should go next to the 6?*

Activity
Children work from Workbook page 43. They work out how many minutes past the hour each number from 1 to 12 represents and stick the appropriate number cards in each position.

Extra help
Make card clock faces available for children who need to move the minute hand as they count around the clock face.

Further extension
Ask children to label *quarter past* and *quarter to*.
Provide a selection of number cards, 0 to 60. Give each child 10 cards and ask them to place each card on the left- or right-hand side of the clock (after half past, before half past) as appropriate. Ask them to compare their answers with another child undertaking the activity.

If you have time
Point to 60. *What other number could go here?* Use a digital clock to show that the number 60 never actually appears on a digital clock because it is then zero minutes past the next hour, that is something o'clock.

Be aware

- Cardboard digital clocks with cards that can be flipped over to show the changing minutes are particularly useful to support the extension activity.

Outcomes

- I can count the minutes in an hour.
- I know how many minutes there are in half an hour.

Supporting resources

- A range of clocks and timers to explore.

Challenge Plan: Year 1

C3: compare capacities; measure capacities using non-standard units; read the time to the hour and half hour; measure time in minutes

---

Summary

Y1 ⭐ C3.6

Time dominoes

Pairs or groups working independently

Year 1 Challenge PCMs 56 and 57

Thin coloured card; scissors; blank dominoes cut from thin card (optional); analogue and digital card clocks (optional)

Abacus Evolve objectives

- **Y2** Read the time to the hour and half hour on analogue and 12-hour digital clocks

Framework objectives

- **Y2** *Use units of time (seconds, minutes, hours, days) and know the relationships between them; read the time to the quarter hour; identify time intervals, including those that cross the hour*
- **Y2** *Ensure everyone contributes, allocate tasks, consider alternatives and reach agreement*

Teacher notes

Preparation
Photocopy PCMs 56 and 57 onto thin card, one copy of each per pair or group of three. Use different coloured card for each pair or group. Cut out the dominoes.

Getting started
Show children the time dominoes and explain how to play if they are not familiar with this type of game. *You must find matching analogue and digital times.* Each child should have six dominoes, with the rest piled nearby.

Activity
Children decide between them who goes first. That child places any domino on the table.
The next child lays a domino on one end, making sure that the two times touching each other are a matching pair. The rest of the group should check that all the dominoes are placed correctly.
Children continue to take turns laying down dominoes at either end of the line.
If a child cannot go, they must pick up another domino from the unused pile, and miss a turn.
The winner is the first child to lay down all their dominoes correctly.

Extra help
Have analogue and digital card clocks available for checking.

Further extension
Children can make some more dominoes to add to the set. They should agree between them which times to use and whether to draw analogue or digital times on each domino. They add the new dominoes to the set and play again. *Does the new set work? Why?* Children can try to play the game aiming to lay the dominoes in a square shape. They place all the dominoes face up. They pick a start domino then choose other dominoes to make a closed square loop. They should try to use as few dominoes as possible.

Be aware

- The number of potential dominoes increases rapidly as more times are included. The set provided therefore only uses a small range of times, allowing children to make and add their own dominoes.

Outcomes

- I can match analogue and digital times for o'clock and half past.

D3: subtracting 1-digit numbers; subtracting multiples of 10; adding two 'teens' numbers'; solving problems involving money

Summary

Y1 ☆ D3.1

On the buses 1

Pairs working independently

Year 1 Challenge Workbook pages 44 and 45

Year 1 Challenge PCMs 58 and 59

Scissors

Abacus Evolve objectives

- Subtract a 1-digit number from a 2-digit number by counting back, not crossing 10
- Subtract a 1-digit number from a 2-digit number by counting back, crossing 10
- Describe position: above, below, beside, left, right

Framework objectives

- Understand subtraction as 'take away' and find a 'difference' by counting up; use practical and informal written methods to support the subtraction of a 1-digit number from a 1-digit or 2-digit number and a multiple of 10 from a 2-digit number
- Take turns to speak, listen to others' suggestions and talk about what they are going to do
- Retell stories, ordering events using story language

Teacher notes

Preparation
Photocopy PCM 58 and PCM 59, one copy of each per pair. Cut out the buses from PCM 58 and the description cards from PCM 59.

Getting started
Ask each pair to open their workbooks at pages 44 and 45. Explain that they are going to work together to take the bus on its route around Jollytown.
Ask each pair to place their bus on the bus terminal. Child A moves it along the route to bus stop 1. Child A looks at the cards from PCM 59 and decides which best describes bus stop 1. They use the words from the card in a sentence. For example: *bus stop 1 is in front of the bakery.* Child A then looks at the queue and counts how many passengers there are waiting. Encourage them to 'see' groups, rather than counting in 1s.
Child B then uses the 'agree' and 'disagree' cards to show whether or not they think that Child A is right.
Explain to pairs that they are going to take turns to do this for each bus stop, until they reach the terminal again.

Activity
Pairs take turns until they complete the route and return to the terminal. They then repeat the route, but with Child B going first. Can pairs sort the cards into the order of the bus route without looking at the workbook pages? Once they have done this, they can check their order against the pictures.

Extra help
Practise the vocabulary on the cards and label each bus stop. Those pupils who are confident speakers can model the language for their partner. This will enable all the children to join in the games later in the week.

Further extension
Answer the questions on the top half of PCM 58.

If you have time
Ask the group to make a bus out of construction blocks and find model people to put into the bus. Encourage children to act out a story about a bus journey, describing each bus stop and the numbers of people who get on and off the bus.
Sing 'The wheels on the bus go round and round' several times, then let the children make up some new verses. Listen to the music if you don't know it (see web link below).

Be aware

- This activity is preparation for playing games using these pages later in the week. The focus is therefore on the language of positioning and sequencing.

Outcomes

- I can describe the bus route and remember what comes next.

Supporting resources

- Children can sing the lyrics to 'The wheels on the bus': http://kids.niehs.nih.gov/lyrics/wheels.htm

Challenge Plan: Year 1

D3: subtracting 1-digit numbers; subtracting multiples of 10; adding two 'teens' numbers'; solving problems involving money

Summary

Y1 ⭐ **D3.2**		**On the buses 2**
		A small group working with an adult
		Year 1 Challenge Workbook pages 44 and 45
		Year 1 Challenge PCMs 58, 60 and 61
		Scissors

 Abacus Evolve objectives

- Subtract a 1-digit number from a 2-digit number by counting back, crossing 10
- Add a 1-digit number to a 2-digit number, crossing a multiple of 10

Framework objectives

- Understand subtraction as 'take away' and find a 'difference' by counting up; use practical and informal written methods to support the subtraction of a 1-digit number from a 1-digit or 2-digit number and a multiple of 10 from a 2-digit number
- Solve problems involving counting, adding, subtracting, doubling or halving in the context of numbers, measures or money, for example to 'pay' and 'give change'

Teacher notes

Preparation
Photocopy PCMs 58, 60 and 61, one copy of each per pair. Cut out the bus from PCM 58 and the number cards from PCM 60.

Activity
- Give each pair their bus. *This is the number 20 bus. How many seats are there? The number 20 bus is only allowed to carry 20 passengers; they must each have a seat.*
- Children open their workbooks at pages 44 and 45. Place the bus on the terminal. Shuffle the number cards and place them in two piles (one pile of + and one pile of −).
- Pairs take turns to move the bus to each stop, describing the route as they go. At each bus stop the player takes a number card from the + or − pile. *If the number says + before it this means the number of people get on the bus at that stop. If the number has − before it this means the number of people get off the bus at that stop. The bus must be full before anyone gets off so only cards from the + pile can be taken until the bus is full.* Children can use PCM 61 to keep a record of how many people are on the bus,
- Once the bus is full, all the passengers must get off by the time the bus gets back to the terminal. Pairs can keep going round the route until the bus has filled up completely and then emptied.

Extra help
Work with a number 12 bus that can only take 12 passengers.

Further extension
Pairs start with 10 passengers in the bus. They can allow passengers to get on or off at each bus stop. One child only takes cards from the + pile and the other child only takes cards from the − pile. Once they have completed the game once, they swap. *Who has the best chance of winning?*

If you have time
Make up your own rules for playing this game with a friend.

Be aware

- This activity is about subtraction as 'one less' or 'two less'. It is important that, if children make number sentences, they relate them to the context.
- Choosing what sort of card to take requires making a link between subtraction and addition. Discuss this with children in the context of the activity.

Outcomes

- I can count forwards and backwards
- I can work with a partner to solve a problem.

Supporting resources

Children can practise subtraction with 'The Number Crew – Ten Thing Bowling':
- http://www.teachers.tv/video/25372

D3: subtracting 1-digit numbers; subtracting multiples of 10; adding two 'teens' numbers'; solving problems involving money

Summary

Y1 ⬠ D3.3   **Football stadium 1**

A small group working with an adult

Year 1 Challenge PCM 62

Scissors

Abacus Evolve objectives	Framework objectives
• Subtract one multiple of 10 from another	• Understand subtraction as 'take away' and find a 'difference' by counting up; use practical and informal written methods to support the subtraction of a 1-digit number from a 1-digit or 2-digit number and a multiple of 10 from a 2-digit number • Describe ways of solving puzzles and problems, explaining choices and decisions orally or using pictures

Teacher notes

Preparation
Photocopy PCM 62, one copy per pair. Cut out the flash cards.

Getting started
Show children the diagram of a football stadium on PCM 62. *This football stadium can seat 100 people. The seating is in blocks of 10 and there are two exits.* Use the flash cards to introduce new words in this context.

Activity
• *At the end of a match, spectators are allowed to leave in blocks so that the exits don't get too busy.*
• *Block E is closest to an exit and leaves first. How many spectators are left?*
• *Now blocks A and B are allowed to leave at the same time. How many spectators are left now?*
• *The rest of the spectators are allowed to leave one or two blocks at a time until the stadium is empty.*
• *How would you organise this? How would you make sure no one is left behind?*
• Allow time for pairs to work together on this problem and then ask each pair to explain their ideas to the group.
• *How many different ways are there to organise the blocks leaving?*

Extra help
Only allow one block to leave the stadium at a time.

Further extension
Allow one, two or three blocks to leave at a time. *How many ways are there of organising the exit now?*

If you have time
Explain that the stadium has doubled in size. *How many spectators can be seated altogether? How could they leave the stadium safely?* Research the capacities of some famous football stadiums. *How many seats in the stadium? How many blocks are the seats organised into?*

Be aware	Outcomes
• Encourage pupils to make informal jottings to support their thinking. They should identify the need for a systematic approach. • Sharing methods and justifying their decisions to the group is important for developing a problem-solving approach within the group.	• I can take 10 or 20 from a multiple of ten. • I can explain my choices using diagrams and pictures.

Supporting resources

Children can check out the capacity of some of the famous football stadiums here:
• http://www.wembleystadium.com/default.aspx

Challenge Plan: Year 1

D3: subtracting 1-digit numbers; subtracting multiples of 10; adding two 'teens' numbers'; solving problems involving money

Summary

Y1 ⭐ D3.4

On the buses 3

Pairs working independently

Year 1 Challenge Workbook pages 44 and 45

Year 1 Challenge PCMs 58 and 60

Scissors; ten 10p coins per pair; four 50p coins per pair

Abacus Evolve objectives

- Subtract one multiple of 10 from another
- Count on and back in 10s from a multiple of 10
- Find totals of sets of coins
- Solve 'real-life' problems involving money (change)

Framework objectives

- Understand subtraction as 'take away' and find a 'difference' by counting up; use practical and informal written methods to support the subtraction of a 1-digit number from a 1-digit or 2-digit number and a multiple of 10 from a 2-digit number
- Solve problems involving counting, adding, subtracting, doubling or halving in the context of numbers, measures or money, for example to 'pay' and 'give change'

Teacher notes

Preparation
Photocopy PCMs 58 and 60, one copy of each per pair. Cut out the buses and the number cards.

Getting started
Children open their workbooks at pages 44 and 45. Place the bus on the bus terminal. Shuffle the number cards and place them in a single pile. *The bus starts off with 10 passengers on board. The fare for any journey is 10p.* Explain the rules of the game.

Activity
Pairs take turns to move their bus around the route. At each stop, a child takes a card from the pile. They add or subtract that number of passengers to or from the bus. For each passenger, they add a 10p coin for the driver.
The bus cannot seat more than 20 passengers, or less than 0. If children pick up a card that takes the total above 20 or below 0, they take another card. When they run out of 10p coins, children swap five 10p coins for a 50p coin. When the bus gets back to the terminal, children work out how much money the driver has.

Extra help
Leave out the money context so that children focus on the numbers of people getting on and off the bus.

Further extension
Imagine that the bus is a double decker and can take double the number of people. The price stays the same for each person. How does this affect the amount of money paid to the driver?

If you have time
Make a bus out of chairs in the play corner. In groups of six, one child is the bus driver and other children are passengers. As children get on the bus they give 10p to the driver. Children count the fare up in 10s.

Be aware

- Children are dealing with two different variables in this activity – people getting on and off the bus and the price that they pay when they get on.
- Children may want to subtract 10p for each passenger that gets off. Explain that passengers do not get a refund so this is not necessary.

Outcomes

- I can solve problems involving adding and subtracting.

Supporting resources

Children can see how many are on board with 'The Number Crew – All Aboard':
- http://www.teachers.tv/video/1763

Challenge Plan: Year 1

D3: subtracting 1-digit numbers; subtracting multiples of 10; adding two 'teens' numbers'; solving problems involving money

Summary

Y1 ⬠ D3.5	**I spy ...**
👤 👤👤	Individuals or pairs working independently
📖	Year 1 Challenge Workbook pages 44 and 45
📓	Year 1 Challenge PCM 63
✂️	Play mat (optional); sand trays (optional); sand (optional)

◁◦◦◦▷ ◦◦◦▷ Abacus Evolve objectives

- Begin to add two 'teens' numbers, not crossing a multiple of 10
- **Y2** Partition 2-digit numbers into T and U
- **Y2** Add two 2-digit numbers using an appropriate strategy

Framework objectives

- Relate addition to counting on; recognise that addition can be done in any order; use practical and informal written methods to support the addition of a 1-digit number or a multiple of 10 to a 1-digit or 2-digit number
- **Y2** *Add or subtract mentally a single-digit number or a multiple of 10 to or from any 2-digit number; use practical and informal written methods to add and subtract 2-digit numbers*
- **Y2** Identify and record the information or calculation needed to solve a puzzle or problem; carry out the steps or calculations and check the solution in the context of the problem

Teacher notes

Preparation
Photocopy PCM 63, one copy for each child.

Getting started
Children open their workbooks to pages 44 and 45. Give each child a copy of PCM 63. Go through the first question on the PCM. *There are 12 people at the park. 11 more arrive. How many now?* Ask children to think about how they could work this out and give suggestions. Demonstrate adding tens first, then units. Read through the other questions on PCM 63 and explain what to do.

Activity
This activity is about close observation and relating simple calculations to a context. Children answer the questions on PCM 63, writing number sentences to show what they have done. When each child has finished their answers they check them with a partner. Pairs discuss whether they agree or disagree with each other's answers. Pairs then make up and complete some number sentences of their own.

Extra help
Ask children to make up number sentences verbally. Pairs work out the number sentence together and record it.
If pupils have difficulty with the calculations, encourage them to draw pictures to explain the sum they are trying to do. If they can make a sentence in words that relates to the picture and makes sense, then that is an important step.

Further extension
Children can create their own questions using the picture on Workbook pages 44 and 45. They look at their number sentences with a partner and sort the questions into groups: take away, add, or something else.

If you have time
Use a play mat and place some objects along the track. Children drive a vehicle along the road and collect each object as they pass. They describe their journey to a partner and make a map of it in sand or a notebook.

Be aware

- Relating number sentences to words and pictures so that they make sense is important.
- Describing what you see or do in words helps to develop speaking and listening skills

Outcomes

- I can describe what I see and use information to solve problems.

Challenge Plan: Year 1

D3: subtracting 1-digit numbers; subtracting multiples of 10; adding two 'teens' numbers'; solving problems involving money

---

Summary

Y1 ☆ D3.6

Football stadium 2

Individuals or pairs working independently

Year 1 Challenge PCMs 62 and 64

10p coins; 1p coins (optional); 5p coins (optional)

◁∘∘∘▷ ∘∘∘▷ Abacus Evolve objectives

- Solve 'real-life' problems involving money (change)
- Add and subtract 9 by adding and subtracting 10
- **Y2** Begin to understand multiplication as repeated addition or as describing an array

Framework objectives

- Solve problems involving counting, adding, subtracting, doubling or halving in the context of numbers, measures or money, for example to 'pay' and 'give change'
- **Y2** Represent repeated addition and arrays as multiplication, and sharing and repeated subtraction (grouping) as division; use practical and informal written methods and related vocabulary to support multiplication and division, including calculations with remainders

---

Teacher notes

Preparation
Photocopy PCMs 62 and 64, one copy of each per pair.

Getting started
Show children the diagram of a football stadium on PCM 62. *To enter the stadium, spectators must go through the turnstile. To get through, spectators have to put a 10p coin into the slot.*
Give children PCM 64 and explain what to do.

Activity
Children work from PCM 64. They answer these questions.
There are currently 10 people in the stadium. How much have they paid in total?
Nine more people enter the stadium. How much money has been paid in total now?
At the end of the match, the turnstile is emptied. It has £100 in it. How many people went to the match? How do you know?

Extra help
Each spectator is charged 1p on entry.

Further extension
Nine people leave the match because of bad weather. They are allowed a refund of 5p. How much money is given back to the spectators? How much money has been collected in total at the turnstiles?

If you have time
Role-play a ticket office in the play corner. Spectators pay 10p to enter.

Be aware

- When adding or subtracting 9 it is easier to add or subtract 10 and then adjust. Using this strategy in the context of money poses an extra challenge.

Outcomes

- I can solve problems using pounds and pence.

Supporting resources

Children can watch 'The Number Crew – Ice Creams' to learn about adding nine:
- http://www.teachers.tv/video/25376

Challenge Plan: Year 1

E3: counting on in 2s or 5s; recognising odd and even numbers; doubling and halving multiples of 5 and 10; halves and quarters

Summary

Y1 ⭐ E3.1	**Counting in 2s and 5s**
	A small group working with an adult
	Year 1 Challenge PCM 65
	Coloured pencils; blank cards; 1–100-squares (optional)

Abacus Evolve objectives

- Count on in 2s or 5s up to 100
- Begin to recognise odd and even numbers up to at least 20

Framework objectives

- *Derive and recall all pairs of numbers with a total of 10 and addition facts for totals to at least 5; work out the corresponding subtraction facts*
- Describe simple patterns and relationships involving numbers or shapes; decide whether examples satisfy given conditions
- Explain their views to others in a small group, and decide how to report the group's views to the class

Teacher notes

Preparation
Photocopy PCM 65, one copy per pair. Cut out the cards on the bottom half of the page.

Activity
- Practise counting together in 2s and 5s.
- Give each pair the top half of PCM 65. Ask them to look at the numbers in the grid, and colour all the numbers they say when they count in 2s, and all the numbers they say when they count in 5s. Ask them to discuss in their pairs the patterns that the numbers make.
- Discuss the terms 'true' and 'false' (and 'odd' and 'even' if necessary) to ensure children understand their meaning.
- Give each pair a set of cards from the bottom half of the PCM. Ask them to play the 'true or false' game:
- Shuffle the cards and place them face down in a pile.
- Children take turns to turn over a card and read it aloud. They say whether the statement is true or false. Their partner says whether or not they agree. Once they have agreed, they put the card in the appropriate pile – they will need one pile for 'true', one pile for 'false', and one pile for 'don't know'.
- Give each child a blank card. Ask them to each write a new sentence about counting in 2s or 5s. Their partner then puts the card on the appropriate pile.
- When each pair has finished, ask them to explain to the rest of the group why they sorted the cards in the way they did. Compare explanations. *Are there any cards that are difficult to sort? Which ones are easy?*

Further extension
Ask pairs to mark the 2s and 5s patterns on a 1–100 square. Ask them to compare the patterns on the 1–100 square with the patterns on the grid on PCM 65. Children should notice that the patterns are not the same. *Why?*

If you have time
Make up true and false statements about other number patterns. Play the game again.

Be aware

- Children may find it difficult to be decisive with true and false. It is possible to play the game using Always true, Sometimes true and Never true. However this can be confusing so using True and False, and allowing a 'Don't know' pile can be a good compromise.

Outcomes

- I can describe a pattern made from counting in 2s and 5s.

Supporting resources

Children can practise sorting statements with the 'Dining Ducks' logic problem:
- http://nrich.maths.org/public/viewer.php?obj_id=2130

E3: counting on in 2s or 5s; recognising odd and even numbers; doubling and halving multiples of 5 and 10; halves and quarters

Summary

Y1 E3.2

Threes

A small group working with an adult

Abacus Evolve objectives

- Begin to count on in 3s from zero

Framework objectives

- *Derive and recall all pairs of numbers with a total of 10 and addition facts for totals to at least 5; work out the corresponding subtraction facts*
- *Describe simple patterns and relationships involving numbers or shapes; decide whether examples satisfy given conditions*
- *Listen to and follow instructions accurately, asking for help and clarification if necessary*

Teacher notes

Activity

- Children sit in groups of three in a circle facing each other. They count on in 3s from 0. (The first child says *0*, the second child says *3*, and the third child says *6*.)
- When each child has had a turn they predict the next number they will count, then continue counting to check if they were right.
- Repeat, but this time ask each child to write down the number after they have said it. Children stop counting when they get to 36. Ask each child to investigate the pattern of numbers they wrote down.
- *What is happening here? Can you predict all the other numbers you will say, up to 60? How did you work out your predictions?*
- Ask each group to count on in 3s from 36 to 60, to check whether their predictions were correct.

Further extension

Ask children to count on in 3s from 60 to 99, then count back in 3s from 99 to 0. Challenge children to explain why each person counts in 9s when three people count in 3s. Children may not be aware why this is happening, but encourage each child to look for and describe the pattern in the numbers they have called out, so that they can predict their next number. Children may describe the pattern in various ways, such as: '*The units are going down 1 and the tens are going up 1.*'

Be aware

- Some children may find it challenging to see patterns. It requires them to notice what is happening to the numbers that they are saying, and to have an awareness of the numbers that other children are saying. They must deal with several different pieces of information at once. Support them in regularly describing what they notice so they do not become overwhelmed.

Outcomes

- I can count in 3s up to 60.
- I can see patterns in numbers and describe them to someone else.
- I can use what I know about number patterns to work out which number will come next.

Supporting resources

Children can practise the 3 times table with this 'Odds and Threes' game:
- http://nrich.maths.org/public/viewer.php?obj_id=1212

Challenge Plan: Year 1

E3: counting on in 2s or 5s; recognising odd and even numbers; doubling and halving multiples of 5 and 10; halves and quarters

Summary

Y1 ⭐ E3.3	**Odds and evens**
	Pairs working independently
	Year 1 Challenge Workbook page 46
	Dice; red and blue colouring pencils; linking cubes (optional)

Abacus Evolve objectives

- Begin to recognise odd and even numbers up to at least 20

Framework objectives

- Describe simple patterns and relationships involving numbers or shapes; decide whether examples satisfy given conditions

Teacher notes

Getting started
Look at the Workbook page. *How can you tell if a number is odd or even?* Discuss children's ideas. Read through the instructions on the Workbook page together.
Give each pair two dice and red and blue colouring pencils.

Activity
Children work from Workbook page 46. They colour the odd numbers on the number track blue and the even numbers red.
They then throw two dice, add the numbers, and work out if the total is odd or even.

Children consider whether the rule *odd + even = odd* is true or false, and explain why. They then make up their own rules about adding odd and even numbers.

Extra help
Ask children to model the numbers they roll on the dice using linking cubes. Demonstrate that if the cubes from the two numbers can be rearranged to form two towers of the same height, then the total is an even number.

Further extension
Children can try to find the odd/even rules for adding three numbers together.

If you have time
Ask children to look for patterns in the set of rules they have written. Can they think of just two rules that describe all four rules they have written?

Information
The rules are:
odd + even = odd; even + odd = odd;
odd + odd = even; even + even = even

These can be expressed by two rules:
If the two numbers are of the same type the total is even.
If the two numbers are of different types, the total is odd.

The rules for adding three numbers together are:
odd + odd + odd = odd;
even + even + even = even;
odd + even + even = odd;
even + odd + odd = even

Be aware

- Odd and even can be difficult to explain in words. However, using a tower of linking cubes for the total and exploring which numbers can form even towers when spilt in two is a good way of visualising odd and even numbers.

Outcomes

- I can recognise odd and even numbers up to 20.
- I can work out the rules for adding odd and even numbers together.

Challenge Plan: Year 1

E3: counting on in 2s or 5s; recognising odd and even numbers; doubling and halving multiples of 5 and 10; halves and quarters

---

Summary

Y1 ⭐ E3.4	**Going for a ride**
	Individuals or pairs working independently
	Year 1 Challenge Workbook page 47
	1p, 2p, 5p and 10p coins; photographs of sit-on rides (optional)

Abacus Evolve objectives

- Exchange coins up to 10p for equivalent in smaller coins
- Recognise coins of different values
- Exchange coins for equivalent in 10p and 1p coins
- Find totals of sets of coins

Framework objectives

- Solve problems involving counting, adding, subtracting, doubling or halving in the context of numbers, measures or money, for example to 'pay' and 'give change'
- Describe ways of solving puzzles and problems, explaining choices and decisions orally or using pictures

---

Teacher notes

Getting started
Look at the Workbook page. Discuss what money Jake has and what money Granddad has. Read through the questions together. Provide plenty of 1p, 2p, 5p and 10p coins.

Activity
Children work from Workbook page 47. They investigate the various combinations of coins Granddad could give Jake in exchange for his 10p coin, so Jake can pay for the ride. Children then think about which combination of coins would not be useful to Jake, and explain their answer. They then work out how much Jake will have left after he has paid for the ride.

Extra help
Ask children to start by working out which coins Jake could put in the slot to pay for the ride (combinations that make 5p).

Further extension
Ask children to find as many ways as they can of making 10p using 1p, 2p and 5p coins.

If you have time
Bring in photographs of sit-on rides to discuss which coins can be used. Think about how long each machine might take for a ride and discuss value for money in this context.

Information
There are three combinations of coins that Granddad can give Jake in exchange for his 10p coin: 4 × 1p and 3 × 2p; 2 × 1p and 4 × 2p; and 5 × 2p. The set of five 2p coins would not be useful to Jake, because they would not allow him to pay exactly 5p for the ride.

Be aware

- Some children find it difficult to understand equivalence in money and may not have had much experience of handling coins. Give children practice by offering plenty of role play opportunities in a play shop.

Outcomes

- I can exchange coins to solve a problem.

Supporting resources

Children can practise exchanging coins of equal value here:
- http://nrich.maths.org/public/viewer.php?obj_id=224

Challenge Plan: Year 1

E3: counting on in 2s or 5s; recognising odd and even numbers; doubling and halving multiples of 5 and 10; halves and quarters

Summary

Y1 ⭐ E3.5

Zina's change

Pairs working independently

Year 1 Challenge PCM 66

1p, 2p, 5p, 10p and 20p coins; 1–50 number track or 1–100 square (optional)

Abacus Evolve objectives

- Find totals of sets of coins and give change
- Solve 'real-life' problems involving money (change)
- Exchange coins up to 10p for equivalent in smaller coins

Framework objectives

- Solve problems involving counting, adding, subtracting, doubling or halving in the context of numbers, measures or money, for example to 'pay' and 'give change'
- Take turns to speak, listen to others' suggestions and talk about what they are going to do

Teacher notes

Preparation
Photocopy PCM 66, one copy per pair.

Getting started
Give each pair the PCM. Go through the questions together. Explain that you would like children to compare answers with another pair when they have finished. Provide plenty of 1p, 2p, 5p, 10p and 20p coins.

Activity
Children work from PCM 66. They work in pairs to decide which item Zina might have bought, and which three coins she would have got as change. They then consider what Zina might have bought if she had been given four coins in change, and what the four coins might be. Children then compare answers with another pair. They should discuss whether they got the same answers, and whether there is more than one right answer for some of the questions.

Extra help
If children are struggling to find the difference between the cost of an item and the amount paid using coins, encourage them to count up on a number track or 1–100 square.

Further extension
Zina buys more than one item. How many options does she have which give three coins in change?

If you have time
Make a play shop. Price up some items for children to buy and sell to practise giving and getting change.

Information
To get three coins in change Zina could buy any of the four items. Buying the biscuits (18p) would give her one 20p, one 10p and one 2p. Buying the teddy (25p) would give her two 10p coins and one 5p coin. Buying the oranges (35p) would give her three 5ps. Buying the football (47p) would give her three 1p coins.

To get four coins in change Zina could have bought the biscuits (18p) and received one 20p, one 10p and two 1ps in change. She could have bought the teddy (25p) and received one 10p coin and three 5p coins. She could have bought oranges (35p) and received one 10p, two 2ps and one 1p.

Be aware

- This activity requires children to think about several steps at once. Some children may need support in identifying the necessary steps.

Outcomes

- I can find totals of sets of coins and give change.

Supporting resources

Children can try another coin problem-solving activity here:
- http://nrich.maths.org/public/viewer.php?obj_id=142

Challenge Plan: Year 1

E3: counting on in 2s or 5s; recognising odd and even numbers; doubling and halving multiples of 5 and 10; halves and quarters

Summary

Y1 ✪ E3.6	**Special offers**
👤 👤👤	Individuals or pairs working independently
📓	Year 1 Challenge PCM 67
✂️🖊️	Plastic coins

Abacus Evolve objectives

- **Y2** Recognise all coins and begin to use £·p notation for money
- **Y2** Find totals of sets of coins: relate to adding three or more numbers
- **Y2** Solve 'real-life' problems involving money (paying an exact sum)

Framework objectives

- **Y2** Solve problems involving addition, subtraction, multiplication or division in contexts of numbers, measures or pounds and pence

Teacher notes

Preparation
Photocopy PCM 67, one copy per child or pair.

Getting started
Explain what a special offer is. *Have you seen anything on special offer?* Look together at the PCM and talk about the special offers on the baked beans. Read through the questions together. Discuss with children how they could check whether a particular offer gives the best value for money.

Activity
Children work from PCM 67. They consider the special offers and find the cheapest way to buy six tins of baked beans. Children then investigate the cheapest way to buy 20 tins of baked beans.

Extra help
To simplify the activity, change the prices so they are less than 10p. Only show one of the special offers. In the second question change 20 tins to 10 tins.

Further extension
This week's special offer on baked beans is buy one tin, get one free. What is the cheapest way of buying 20 tins this week?

Information
The cheapest way to buy six tins of baked beans is to buy two packs of 3 tins (54p). The cheapest way to buy 20 tins is to buy six packs of 3 tins and one pack of 2 tins (£1·82).

Be aware

- The second question requires children to deal with numbers over 100, and amounts of money greater than one pound. They may need help with converting answers in pence into pounds and pence.

Outcomes

- I can add more than two numbers together to compare prices.

Supporting resources

Children can practise giving the correct change in this 'Christmas shopping' activity:
- http://nrich.maths.org/public/viewer.php?obj_id=162

PCM Contents

1	Finders keepers	35	Making dice: flash cards
2	Coin collector	36	Game board
3	Round and round	37	The shape sorter
4	Six in a line: questions	38	Fill the box
5	Six in a line: bingo cards	39	First to 12 game
6	Spiral worms	40	Four dice
7	Days of the week	41	Number cards: tens and ones
8	Week wheel	42	Apple packing
9	Month wheel	43	Caterpillars
10	My group of _____	44	Choosing tracks
11	Shape labels	45	Take-away menu
12	Squares and rectangles	46	Number lines
13	Circles and triangles	47	Fives
14	What's my picture?	48	Adding tens game board
15	Shape families 1	49	Adding tens spinner
16	Shape families 2	50	Chasing 9
17	Labels for shape families	51	Numbers, words and pictures
18	Skittles	52	Missing digits
19	Next door numbers	53	Rice mice game
20	Paying for parking	54	Half past
21	Money changer	55	How many minutes?
22	Colouring to order	56	Time dominoes 1
23	Hidden numbers 1	57	Time dominoes 2
24	Hidden numbers 2	58	On the buses 1
25	Shortcuts	59	On the buses: description cards
26	What's my number?	60	On the buses: number cards
27	Turning around	61	On the buses 2
28	Obstacle course	62	Football stadium 1
29	How heavy is a ball?	63	I spy…
30	How heavy is a ____?	64	Football stadium 2
31	Grams or kilograms?	65	Counting in 2s and 5s
32	Analogue o'clock cards	66	Zina's change
33	Digital o'clock cards	67	Special offers
34	Coin pictogram		

Finders keepers

Abacus Evolve Year 1 Challenge PCM © Pearson Education Ltd 2009

Start

→

Finish

10p bank

?

?

?

Coin collector

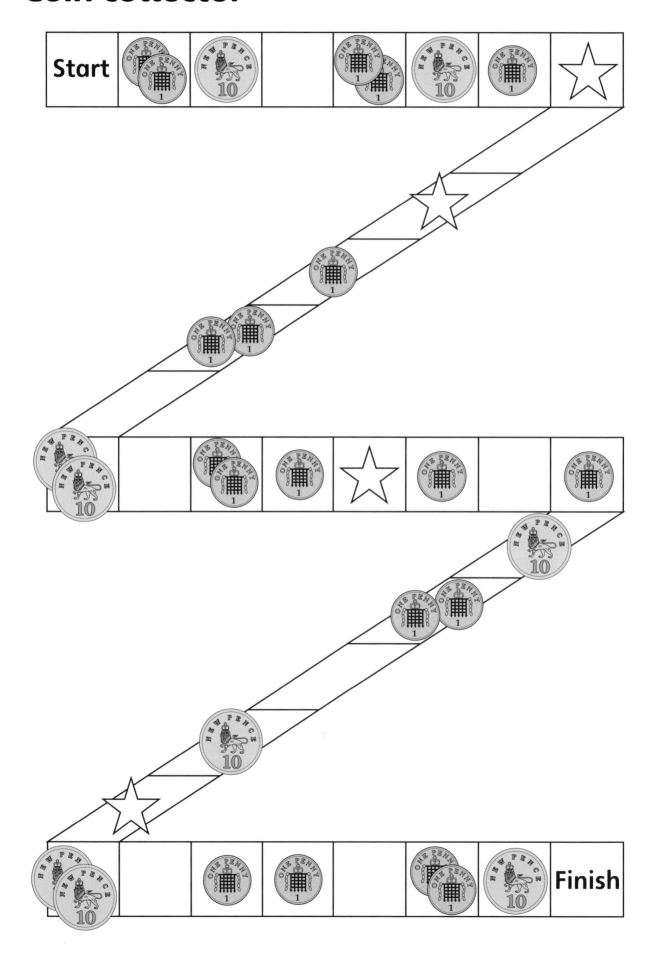

Round and round

- You should each have six 1p coins in a bag.
- Sit in a circle. Write your names in the table.
- Write how much money you each have.
- Write how much money you have in total.
- Throw a dice. Pass that many coins to the next player.
- Have a turn each.
- Write how much money you have now, and the total.
- Play four rounds.

Players' names	Start	Round 1	Round 2	Round 3	Round 4
1					
2					
3					
4					
5					
6					
7					
8					
Total					

Abacus Evolve Year 1 Challenge PCM © Pearson Education Ltd 2009

Six in a line: questions

$5 + 1 =$	$8 - 2 =$	$6 - 1 =$
$6 - 0 =$	$4 + 2 =$	$10 + 2 =$
$6 + 0 =$	$1 + 5 =$	$2 + 4 =$
$6 - 2 =$	$6 - 1 =$	$7 - 1 =$
$6 - 3 =$	$1 + 5 =$	$8 - 2 =$
$3 + 3 =$	$2 + 6 =$	$9 - 3 =$
$10 - 4 =$	$4 + 2 =$	$12 - 6 =$
Half of 12?	Double 3?	Double 6?
2 apples and 4 more apples. How many altogether?	I have 10p and spend 4p. How much do I have left?	Jane is 5 years old. How old will she be on her next birthday?
How many spots are there on a 'double 3' domino?	How many spots are there on two dice when a double 6 is thrown?	I have £3 in my purse and £3 in my piggy bank. How much altogether?

Six in a line: bingo cards

Abacus Evolve Year 1 Challenge PCM © Pearson Education Ltd 2009

6	4	7	7	5	6
6	6	6	6	6	6
50	6	6	6	4	6
12	40	6	6	9	6
6	6	6	6	6	6
6	5	4	3	60	6

6	4	70	7	0	6
6	6	6	6	6	6
50	6	6	6	9	6
12	40	6	6	9	6
6	6	6	6	6	6
6	9	8	33	60	6

6	4	70	7	0	6
6	6	6	6	6	2
50	6	6	6	6	3
12	40	6	6	9	4
6	6	6	6	6	5
6	9	8	33	60	6

6	9	9	7	0	6
6	9	6	6	6	6
9	6	6	6	9	6
12	9	6	6	9	6
6	6	6	6	6	6
6	9	8	9	60	6

6	4	7	7	5	6
6	6	6	6	6	6
50	6	6	6	4	6
12	40	6	6	9	6
6	6	6	6	6	6
6	5	4	3	60	6

6	4	7	7	5	6
6	6	6	6	6	6
50	6	6	6	4	6
12	40	6	6	9	6
6	6	6	6	6	6
6	5	4	3	60	6

Spiral worms

Write each worm's name under its picture.
Bo is shorter than Sol.
Sol is longer than Wes.
Jeb is the longest worm.
Wes is shorter than Bo.

Which worm is which?

_____

_____

_____

_____

Days of the week

Monday	Monday
Tuesday	Tuesday
Wednesday	Wednesday
Thursday	Thursday
Friday	Friday
Saturday	Saturday
Sunday	Sunday

Abacus **Evolve** Year 1 Challenge PCM © Pearson Education Ltd 2009

Week wheel

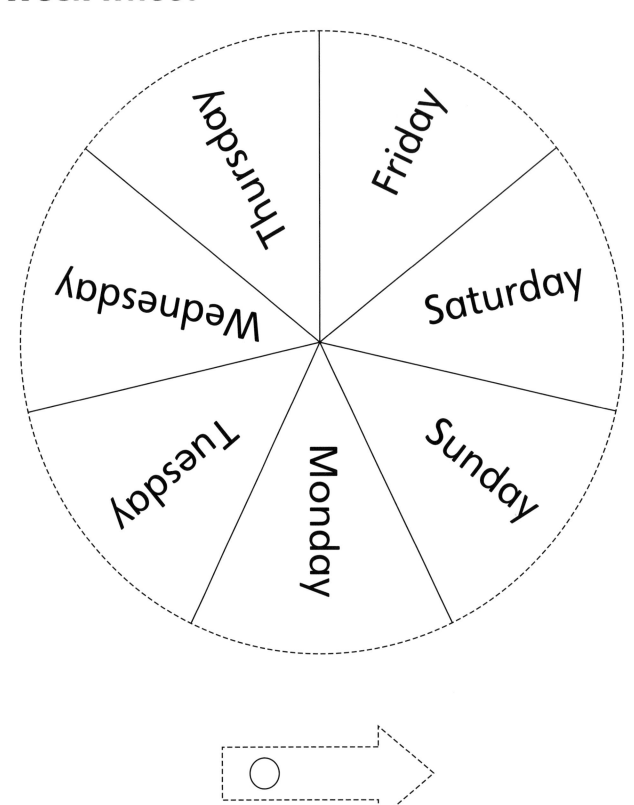

Month wheel

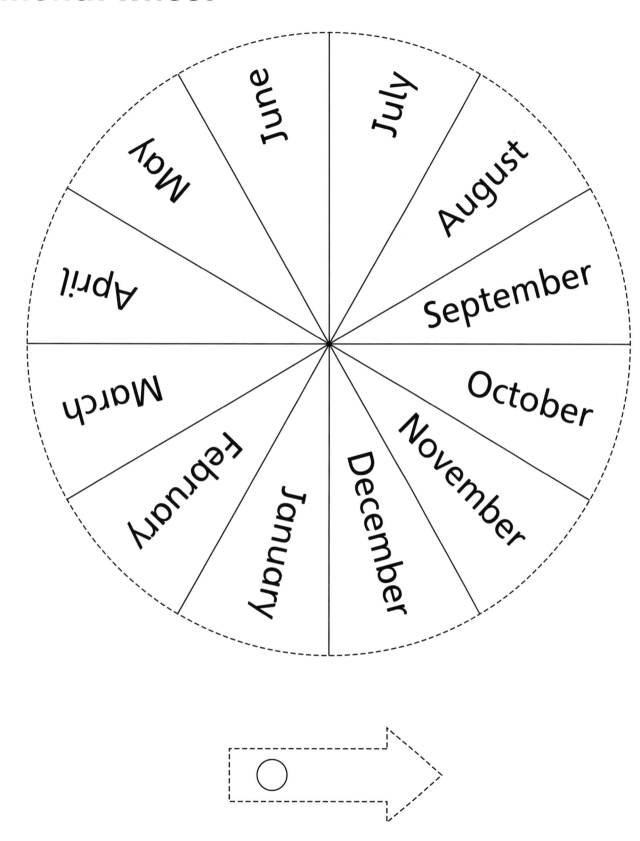

Abacus Evolve Year I Challenge PCM © Pearson Education Ltd 2009

My group of _____

Stick the shapes you have collected in the box.

Shape labels

Cut along the dotted lines and fold along the solid lines.

rectangle	square
triangle	circle
Why?	Because...

Abacus Evolve Year I Challenge PCM © Pearson Education Ltd 2009

Squares and rectangles

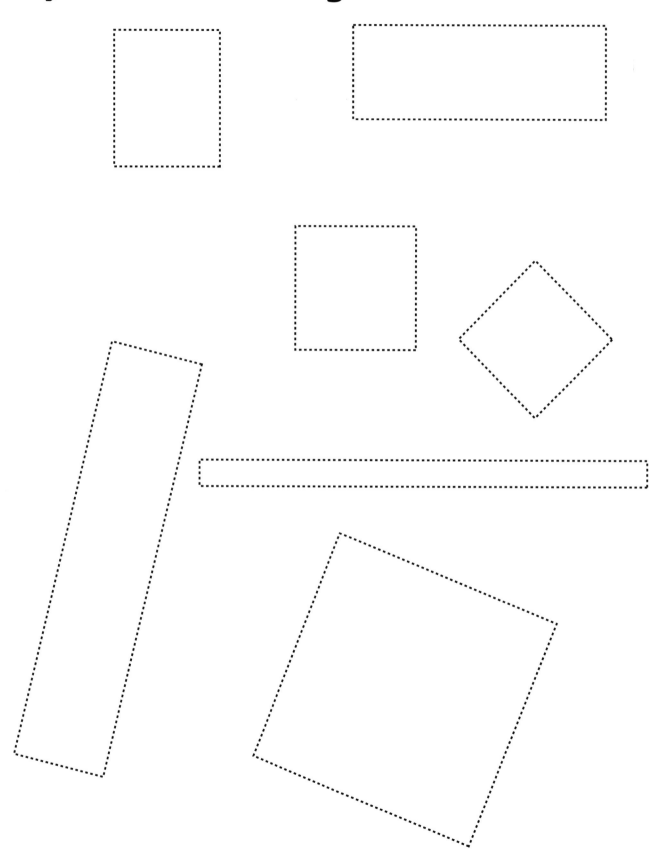

Circles and triangles

Abacus Evolve Year I Challenge PCM © Pearson Education Ltd 2009

What's my picture?

Shape families I

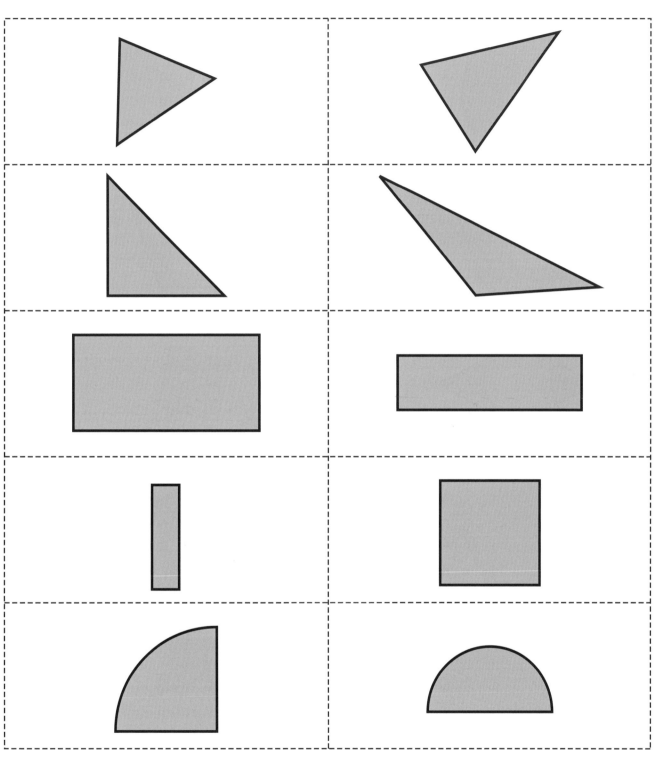

Abacus Evolve Year I Challenge PCM © Pearson Education Ltd 2009

Shape families 2

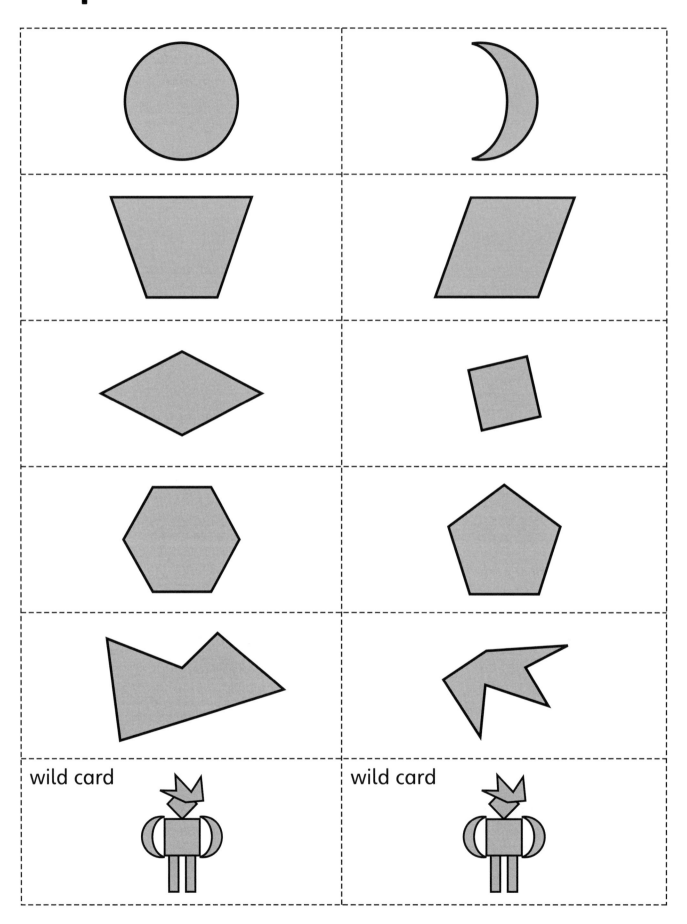

Labels for shape families

Abacus Evolve Year I Challenge PCM © Pearson Education Ltd 2009

rectangles	quadrilaterals
squares	triangles
curved	straight
polygons	shapes with more than four sides
shapes with less than four sides	shapes with right angles

Skittles

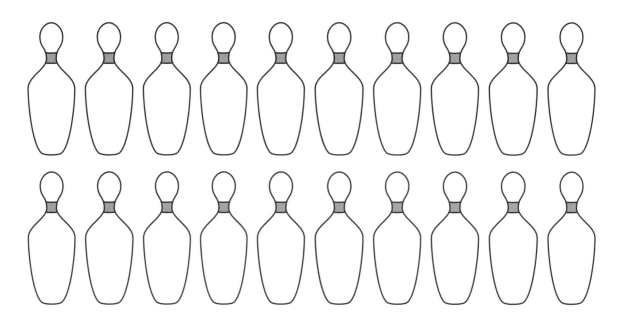

Take turns to throw a dice. Cross out the matching number of skittles.
The winner is the one to cross out the last skittle.

Score card

First to 0
You start with 20
Who wins this time?

Use this number line to help you.

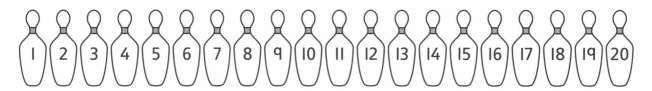

Abacus Evolve Year I Challenge PCM © Pearson Education Ltd 2009

Next door numbers

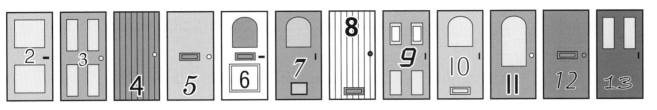

Amina and Ben play a game. Amina chooses two numbers next door to each other. She adds them using doubles.

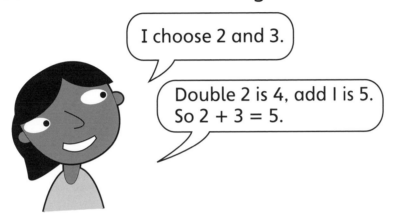

I choose 2 and 3.

Double 2 is 4, add I is 5.
So 2 + 3 = 5.

Amina scores 5 points. She puts a cross on doors 2 and 3. They can't be used again. Now it is Ben's turn.

Play Amina and Ben's game until there are no more pairs of next door numbers. Add your scores. The player with the higher total wins the game.

Name:		Name:	
Doubling sum	Score	Doubling sum	Score
Total		Total	

Paying for parking

1 hour - 10p
2 hours -15p
Coins accepted
1p 2p 5p 10p

12:00

Mr Biggs wants to park his car for an hour.
He has 1p, 2p and 5p coins.

How many different ways could Mr Biggs pay for his ticket?

_____

Show how you worked out the answer.

Mr Biggs checks the time on the ticket machine.
What time must he be back at his car?

_____

Mrs Ghosh parks her car at the same time as Mr Biggs.
She will not be back until 2pm.
How many hours does she need to pay for? _____ hours

She has 1p, 2p, 5p and 10p coins in her purse.
How many different ways could she pay for her ticket?

_____

Show how you worked out the answer.

Money changer

This is a change machine.
It changes Ips and 2ps into 10p coins.

Mr Jin has 20 coins in his pocket.
They are either Ips or 2ps.

Abacus Evolve Year I Challenge PCM © Pearson Education Ltd 2009

Mr Jin puts 10 coins into the machine.
He gets two 10p coins.

Which coins did he put in? _____

Mr Jin has 10 coins left. He buys a newspaper for 12p.
He now has four coins left.

Which coins did he use? _____

Mr Jin buys some coffee for 7p. He gets Ip change.

How much money does he have left? _____

Make up some more questions using the change machine.
Ask your partner to answer them.

Colouring to order

Ist first	**2nd** second	**3rd** third	**4th** fourth
5th fifth	**6th** sixth	**7th** seventh	**8th** eighth
9th ninth	**10th** tenth	**IIth** eleventh	**12th** twelfth
13th thirteenth	**14th** fourteenth	**15th** fifteenth	**16th** sixteenth
17th seventeenth	**18th** eighteenth	**19th** nineteenth	**20th** twentieth

Abacus Evolve Year 1 Challenge PCM © Pearson Education Ltd 2009

Hidden numbers 1

$6 + 2 = 8$

$3 + 5 = 8$

$1 + 7 = 8$

$5 + 3 = 8 + 0$

$4 + 4 = 7 + 1$

$6 + 2 = 3 + 5$

Hidden numbers 2

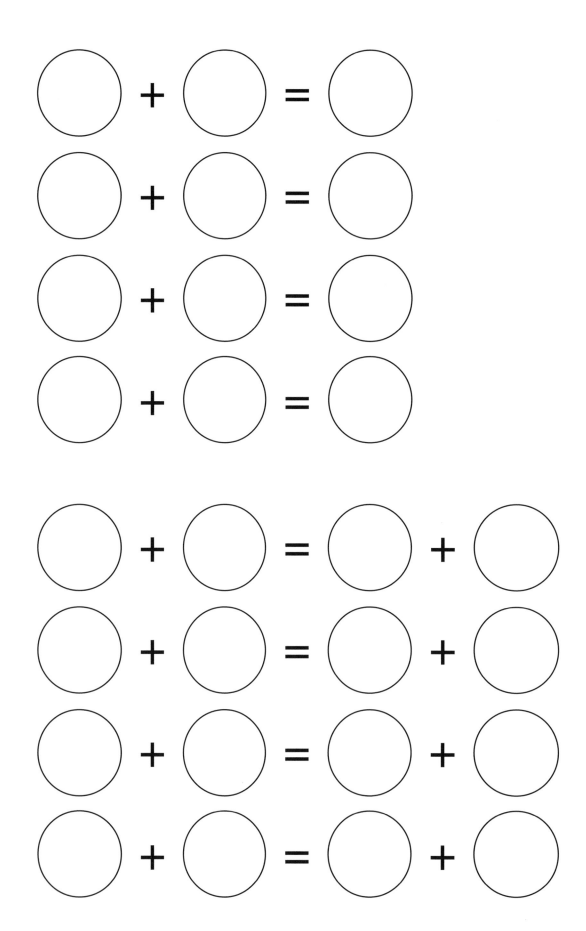

Shortcuts

Rafael has found a shortcut for answering all the questions on the board.

Write some questions that have a shortcut.
Use any numbers from 0 to 10 in your questions.

Can someone else spot the shortcut?

Explain your shortcut.

Abacus Evolve Year I Challenge PCM © Pearson Education Ltd 2009

What's my number?

10	12	13	26
28	15	24	33
34	16	23	31
30	21	20	18

Turning around

Find some objects and sort them in this table.

Turns a whole turn or more	Turns less than a whole turn

Now see if you can find some things that turn a half turn.

Turns a half turn	Turns less than a half turn

Abacus Evolve Year I Challenge PCM © Pearson Education Ltd 2009

Obstacle course

Place five items on this grid to make an obstacle course.
Choose a start point.
Challenge a partner to visit all the obstacles using the shortest path possible

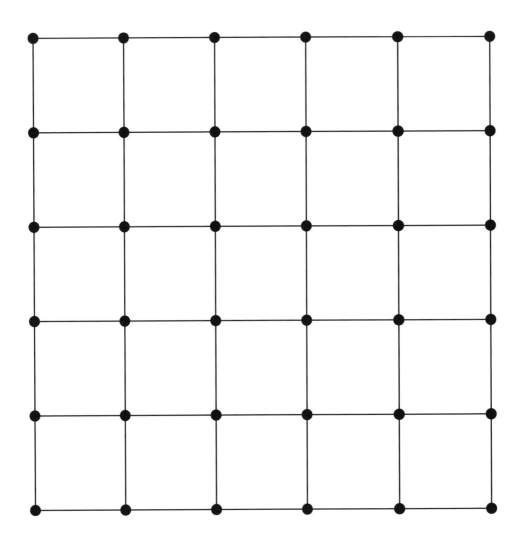

What is the smallest number of steps needed to visit all the obstacles?

How heavy is a ball?

Colour this ball to make
it look the same as yours.

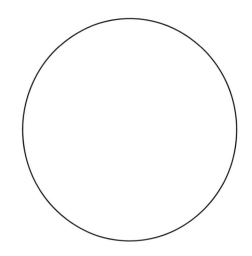

How heavy is your ball? Estimate first, then measure.

estimate ☐

actual ☐

estimate ☐

actual ☐

estimate ☐

actual ☐

estimate ☐

actual ☐

Were your guesses close?

Whose ball is the lightest? _____

Whose ball is the heaviest? _____

Put all the balls in a line, in order of weight.

How do you know?

Abacus Evolve Year 1 Challenge PCM © Pearson Education Ltd 2009

How heavy is a _____ ?

Draw the object you are going to weigh.

How heavy is your object? Guess first, then measure.

estimate ☐

actual ☐

estimate ☐

actual ☐

estimate ☐

actual ☐

estimate ☐

actual ☐

Is your object lighter or heavier than your ball?

How do you know?

_____

Grams or kilograms?

Find six items you would measure in grams.
Find six items you would measure in kilograms.
Draw them below.

Measure in grams		Measure in kilograms	

Weigh the items in grams or kilograms.

Label the lightest object I, the next lightest 2, and so on until you
label the heaviest object I2.

How heavy do you think a kilogram is,
compared to a gram?

Abacus Evolve Year I Challenge PCM © Pearson Education Ltd 2009

Analogue o'clock cards

Digital o'clock cards

Abacus Evolve Year I Challenge PCM © Pearson Education Ltd 2009

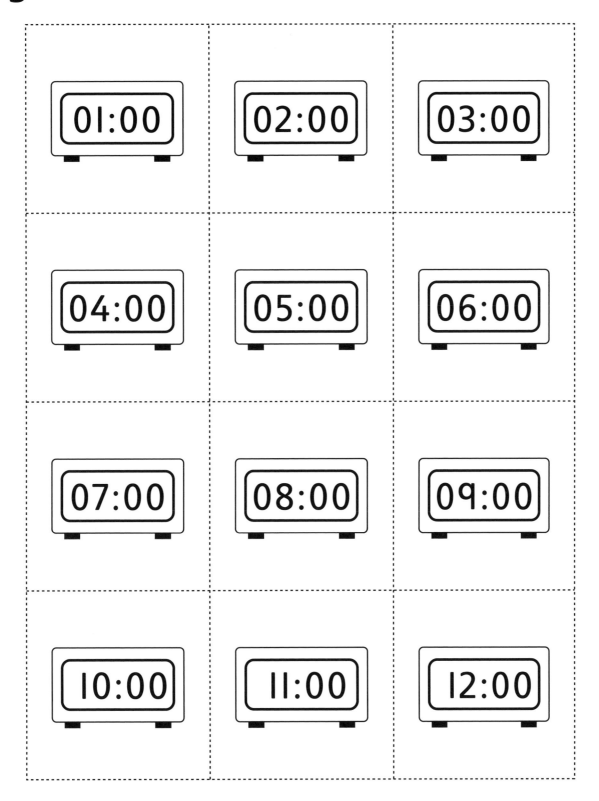

Coin pictogram

20p	10p	5p	2p	1p

What questions can you ask about your pictogram?

Making dice: flash cards

Abacus Evolve Year I Challenge PCM © Pearson Education Ltd 2009

cube	cuboid	sphere
pyramid	triangle	square
face	rectangle	circle

Game board

20	Finish	
19		
18	17	16
		15
12	13	14
11		
10	9	8
		7
4	5	6
3		
2	1	Start

The shape sorter

Answer the questions and follow the arrows.

Put your 4 shapes in this box.
Ask a question to sort the shapes into 2 groups.

_____

_____

Yes

No

Put all the shapes with a Yes answer to the question in here.

Put all the shapes with a No answer to the question in here.

Here are some questions you might ask:
Does it roll?
Does it have flat surfaces?

What else could you ask about your shapes?

Abacus Evolve Year 1 Challenge PCM © Pearson Education Ltd 2009

Fill the box

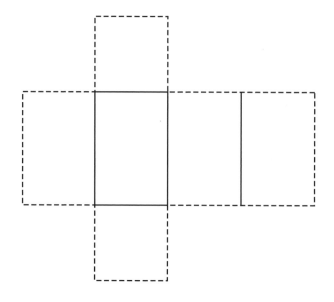

1	2	1
2	1	2
1	2	1
2	1	2
1	2	1

Abacus Evolve Year 1 Challenge PCM © Pearson Education Ltd 2009

First to 12 game

How to play
Player 1: write *1* or *2*.
Player 2: add 1 or 2. Find the total.
Keep taking turns to add 1 or 2 and find the running total.
The winner is the first one who gets to 12.

Example

Player 1	Player 2
2	3
5	
12	

Who do you think will be the first one who gets to 12? Why?

_____

Finish this game and see if you are right.

Play the game with your partner.

Name:	Name:
12	

Who won? What would you do differently next time? Why?

_____

_____

Four dice

Are there any easy ways to add up these dice numbers?

Throw four dice.
Record the numbers in the boxes.
Add up the numbers and write the total.

6	1	6	1	Total 14

Now try this yourself. Do it four times.

				Total
				Total
				Total
				Total

Did you find any easy ways to find the totals?

Swap sheets with a partner. Check each other's totals.
Take turns to explain how you worked them out.
Did you both do it the same? How else could you have done it?

_____

What is the lowest possible total of four dice numbers? _____

What is the highest? _____

Number cards: tens and ones

Abacus Evolve Year I Challenge PCM © Pearson Education Ltd 2009

10	20	30	40
50	10	20	30
40	50	1	2
3	4	5	6
7	8	9	10
10	1	2	5

Apple packing

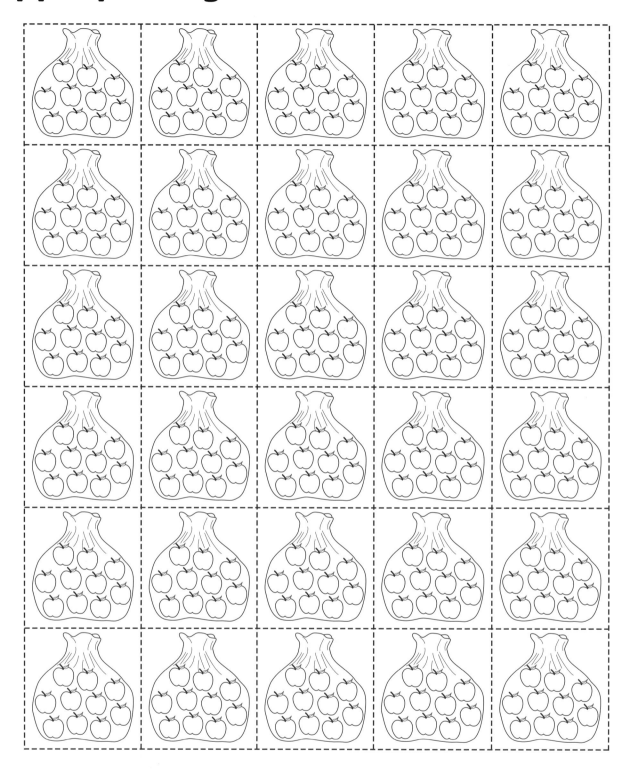

Caterpillars

The numbers on this caterpillar follow a pattern.

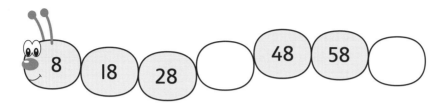

What rule does the number pattern follow? _____
Fill in the missing numbers.

- Throw two dice. Add the numbers together. Write the answer on the caterpillar's head.
- Use the 'add 10' rule to fill in the rest of the numbers.

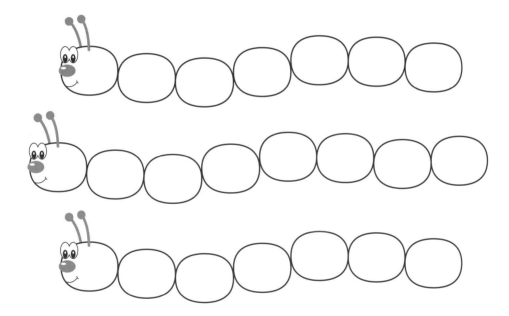

What number will be on this caterpillar's head? _____

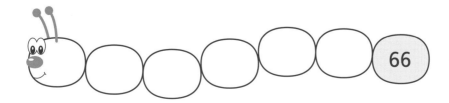

Check your answer by filling in the missing numbers.

Abacus Evolve Year I Challenge PCM © Pearson Education Ltd 2009

Choosing tracks

Record your scores from the game here.

Name	Name	Name
Total score	Total score	Total score

Take-away menu

Abacus Evolve Year I Challenge PCM © Pearson Education Ltd 2009

Tina's Take-away Treats

Meals		Side orders	
Sausage, egg and chips	26p	Chips	5p
Chicken curry and rice	36p	Rice	6p
Pizza and garlic bread	45p	Garlic bread	4p
		Sausage	15p

Work out how much each order costs.

Lujan would like just pizza.

Kofi would like egg and chips.

Sally would like chicken curry with chips instead of rice.

Make up some more orders.
Ask a partner to work out the cost.

Number lines

There are 2 packs of pencils with
12 pencils in each pack.
4 pencils are missing.

How many pencils are left?

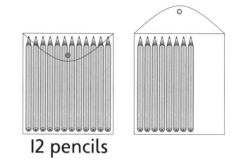

12 pencils

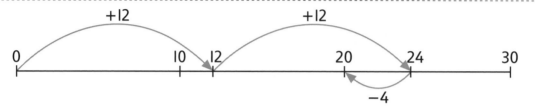

There are 4 bags of carrots with
10 carrots in each bag. A rabbit
has eaten all the carrots in one
bag.

How many carrots are left?

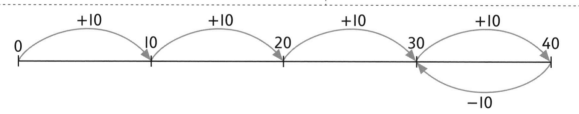

There are 7 boxes of crackers with
5 crackers in each box. 2 boxes
each have 3 crackers missing.

How many crackers are left?

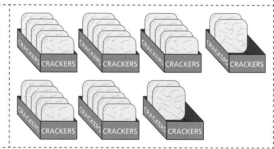

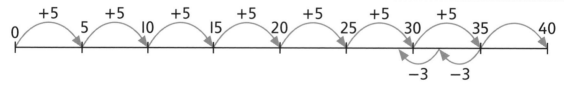

Abacus Evolve Year 1 Challenge PCM © Pearson Education Ltd 2009

Fives

Colour the 'hand' numbers on the 1–100 square.

1	2	3	4	5	6	7	8	9	10
11	12	13	14	15	16	17	18	19	20
21	22	23	24	25	26	27	28	29	30
31	32	33	34	35	36	37	38	39	40
41	42	43	44	45	46	47	48	49	50
51	52	53	54	55	56	57	58	59	60
61	62	63	64	65	66	67	68	69	70
71	72	73	74	75	76	77	78	79	80
81	82	83	84	85	86	87	88	89	90
91	92	93	94	95	96	97	98	99	100

What do you notice about the pattern?

Fill in the boxes on the number line.

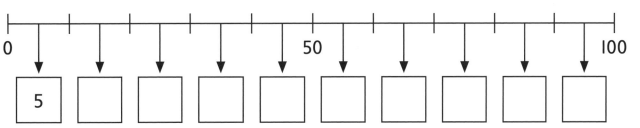

What do you notice about the patterns?

Adding 10s game board

31	32	33	34	35	36	37	38	39	40
41	42	43	44	45	46	47	48	49	50
51	52	53	54	55	56	57	58	59	60
61	62	63	64	65	66	67	68	69	70
71	72	73	74	75	76	77	78	79	80
81	82	83	84	85	86	87	88	89	90
91	92	93	94	95	96	97	98	99	100
101	102	103	104	105	106	107	108	109	110
111	112	113	114	115	116	117	118	119	120

Adding 10s spinner

Abacus Evolve Year 1 Challenge PCM © Pearson Education Ltd 2009

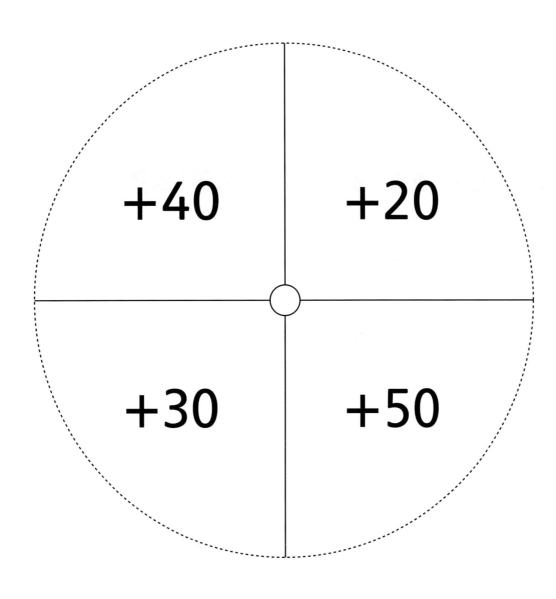

+40 +20

+30 +50

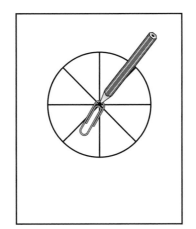

Chasing 9

- Throw the two dice.

- Find the total. Is it close to 9?

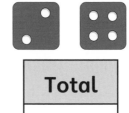

Total
6

3 from 9

- If you are happy with your throw, record how far it is from 9.

- If you are not happy with your throw, you can throw one or both of the dice again.

Total
10

1 from 10

- Find the total. Record how far it is from 9.

Take turns, writing your totals in the table.
The winner is the player whose total score is closer to 0.

Turn	Player A		Player B	
	Total	How far from 9?	Total	How far from 9?
I				
2				
3				
4				
5				
	Score:		Score:	

Numbers, words and pictures

Abacus Evolve Year 1 Challenge PCM © Pearson Education Ltd 2009

6p + 3p = 9p	Yes
5p + 1p + 3p = 9p	2 × 6 eggs
2p + 2p + 2p + 3p = 9p	2 × 6 = 12 eggs
(3 × 2p) + 3p = 9p	Half of 12 eggs = 6
Mum is only eating 3 portions a day.	9 pages
Mum isn't eating enough fruit and vegetables.	10 × 9 = 90
Mum needs 1 more portion on day 1 and 3 more portions on day 2.	90 ÷ 9 = 10 pages
(4 + 1) + (2 + 3) = 10	90 ÷ 10 = 9

Missing digits

Fill in the missing digits.

$1 \bigcirc + 3 = \bigcirc 5$ $1 \bigcirc + 3 = \bigcirc 0$

$\bigcirc 9 + 2 = 2 \bigcirc$ $25 + \bigcirc = \bigcirc 0$

$\bigcirc 6 + \bigcirc = \bigcirc 3$

$\bigcirc 5 + \bigcirc = \bigcirc 1$

$32 + \bigcirc 8 = \bigcirc 0$

$24 + \bigcirc 6 = \bigcirc 0$

What do you notice about these number sentences?

_____

_____

Make up some missing-number sentences for a partner.

Rice mice game

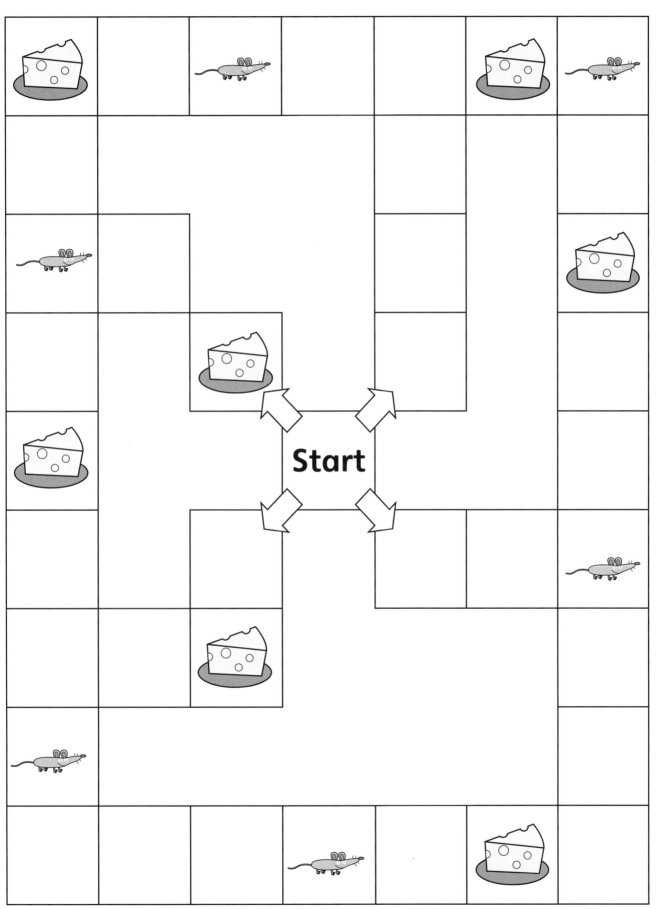

Abacus Evolve Year 1 Challenge PCM © Pearson Education Ltd 2009

Half past

1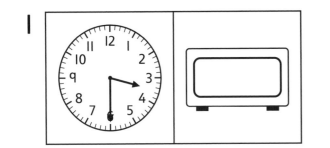

2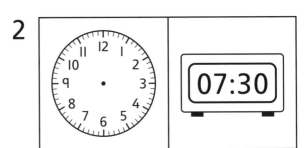

3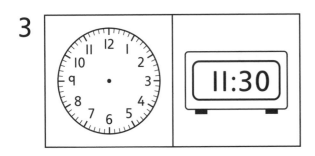

4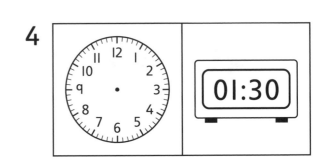

5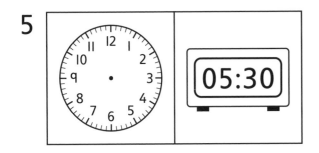

6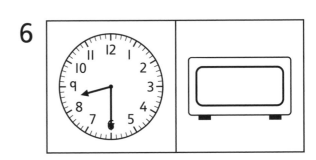

7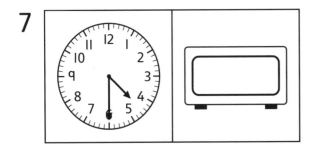

8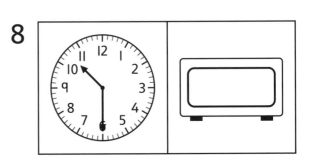

q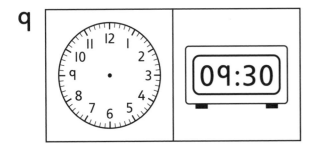

10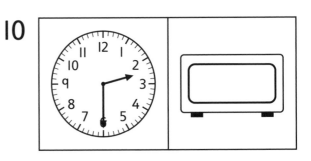

Abacus Evolve Year I Challenge PCM © Pearson Education Ltd 2009

How many minutes?

5	25	45	15
40	10	50	60
35	55	20	30

35	25	5	20
10	45	55	30
50	60	40	15

Time dominoes I

08:00	(clock)	12:00	02:30
(clock)	(clock)	11:30	(clock)
06:30	04:30	(clock)	(clock)
10:00	(clock)	01:30	(clock)
08:00	01:30	(clock)	04:30
(clock)	02:30	(clock)	(clock)
12:00	(clock)	06:30	10:00
(clock)	(clock)	11:30	(clock)

Time dominoes 2

Abacus *Evolve* Year 1 Challenge PCM © Pearson Education Ltd 2009

04:30	(clock)	08:00	02:30
(clock)	(clock)	11:30	(clock)
06:30	12:00	(clock)	(clock)
10:00	(clock)	01:30	(clock)
04:30	01:30	(clock)	08:00
(clock)	02:30	(clock)	(clock)
12:00	(clock)	06:30	10:00
(clock)	(clock)	11:30	(clock)

On the buses I

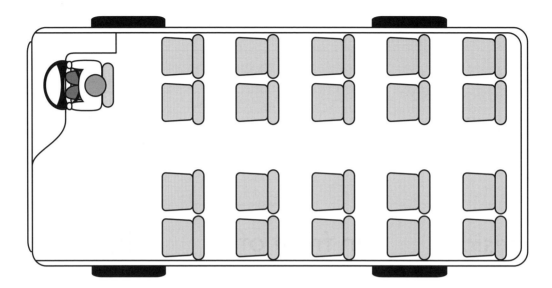

How many people can fit in the bus?

_____

How many people are at each bus stop?

_____

_____

_____

How many people in total are waiting?

_____

Will everyone fit on the bus?

_____

_____

_____

Cut out the little bus.
Drive it around the town on Workbook pages 44 and 45.
Stop at each bus stop and describe where it is.
Use the cards from PCM 59 to help you.

Abacus Evolve Year I Challenge PCM © Pearson Education Ltd 2009

On the buses: description cards

next to	opposite	near
beside	in front of	by
at	behind	left
right	above	below
in the corner	agree	disagree

On the buses: number cards

+1	+2	+3	+4
+5	+6	+7	+8
+9	+10	−10	−9
−8	−7	−6	−5
−4	−3	−2	−1

On the buses 2

Keep a record of the number of people on the bus each time you stop at a bus stop.

Bus stop	Number of people on the bus
Bus terminal	0
1	
2	
3	
4	
5	
6	
Bus terminal	

Abacus Evolve Year I Challenge PCM © Pearson Education Ltd 2009

Football stadium 1

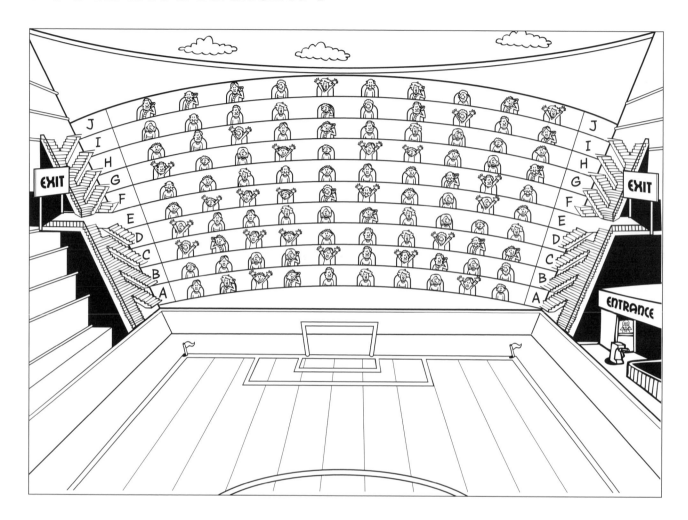

stadium	blocks
exit	entry
spectator	ticket office

I spy ...

Look at Workbook pages 44 and 45.

There are 12 people at the park. 11 more arrive

How many now? _12 + 11 = 23_____

There are 14 cars in the garage. 13 more arrive.

How many now? _____

There are 18 buses in the terminal. 14 more arrive.

How many now? _____

There are 15 buns in the bakery. 19 more are delivered.

How many now? _____

Swap with a partner. Do you have the same answers?

Work with a partner to make up some number sentences of your own.

Abacus Evolve Year 1 Challenge PCM © Pearson Education Ltd 2009

Football stadium 2

Look at the picture of the stadium on PCM 62.
Find the turnstile. To get through the turnstile, spectators put a
10p coin into the slot.

There are 10 people in the stadium. How much money have they
put into the turnstile?

_____

Nine more people arrive at the stadium and pay at the turnstile.
In total how much money has been put into the turnstile now?

_____

_____

At the end of the match, the turnstile has £100 in it.
How many people went to the match?
How do you know?

_____

_____

_____

Counting in 2s and 5s

1	2	3	4	5
6	7	8	9	10
11	12	13	14	15
16	17	18	19	20
21	22	23	24	25
26	27	28	29	30
31	32	33	34	35
36	37	38	39	40

Colour all the numbers you say when you count in 2s.

Circle all the numbers you say when you count in 5s.

What patterns can you see?

_____

_____

_____

_____

_____

When you count in 5s all the numbers are even.	When you count in 5s all the numbers end in 5.	When you count in 5s all the numbers end in an even digit.
When you count in 5s all the numbers end in a 0 or a 5.	When you count in 2s some numbers are odd.	When you count in 2s all the numbers are even.
Some numbers are the same when you count in 2s and 5s.	Some numbers in the 5s pattern are also in the 2s pattern.	The number 200 is in both the 2s pattern and the 5s pattern.

Abacus Evolve Year I Challenge PCM © Pearson Education Ltd 2009

Zina's change

Zina buys just one item. She gives the shopkeeper a 50p coin.

Zina gets three coins in change. What might she have bought?

_____

_____

Which three coins might she have got in change?

_____

If Zina got four coins in change, what might she have bought?

_____

_____

Which four coins might she have got in change?

_____

Special offers

There are some special offers on baked beans today.

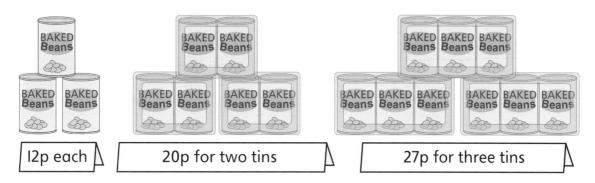

| 12p each | 20p for two tins | 27p for three tins |

Ella needs six tins of beans.
What is the cheapest way to buy them?

_____

_____

Dillon needs 20 tins of beans.
What is the cheapest way to buy them?

_____

_____

But Dillon sees another special offer.
How many tins of beans should Dillon get?

BAKED Beans
Buy 10 cans get one FREE

_____

_____

_____

Abacus Evolve Year 1 Challenge PCM © Pearson Education Ltd 2009